the Whole Enchilada

A Spicy Collection of Sylvia's Best

the whole enchilada

A Spicy Collection of Sylvia's Best
by Nicole Hollander

BLOOMSBURY

First published in Great Britain in 1993

Bloomsbury Publishing Ltd, 2 Soho Square, London W1V 5DE

A CIP catalogue record for this book is available from the
British Library

ISBN 0 7475 1619 7

Book designed by Tom Greensfelder and Steve Strong

Printed in Great Britain by St Edmundsbury Press, Suffolk

Contents

I know that I loved the comics. I learned to read so that I could read the Sunday comics without my parents' help (although someone once pointed out that my favorite cartoons, *The Little King* and *Henry* didn't have any words). I know I stopped reading comics, but I can't remember why. I have a friend who, when she can't remember something like the sixties, says: "Well, I grew up in Mexico." I usually say: "Well, I was married at the time" to explain the gaps in my memory from ages five to 27.

Maybe the comics stopped being relevant to my life because they were all written by men, filled with male characters. But then I always thought I would grow up to be Lew Archer (a private eye and the friend of those who have no friends). How come I never noticed there was a gender difference?

Well one thing I do know, I know where Sylvia came from. Here's a picture of her. She's the one who's looking worldly and weary and smoking a long cigarette. I'm the smaller one, grinning in the background. My grandmother, my mother, and all her friends were witty; in my neighborhood, women had all the best lines. Sylvia is all of them: Annie, Bessie, Shirley, Esther, Goldie, Jennie, Rosie, Lee and Irma.

My mother and father at a Las Vegas night club. Variations of my mother's hat and the fashions of her youth keep popping up in Sylvia.

The Spokeswoman was a national, Chicago-based feminist publication.

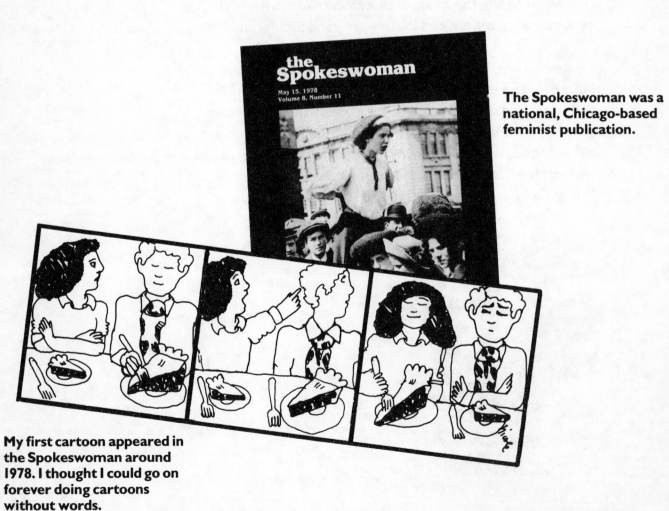

My first cartoon appeared in the Spokeswoman around 1978. I thought I could go on forever doing cartoons without words.

The 1970's prototype Sylvia
—not yet named, her politics
a little shaky, her profile
undeveloped, but with
backless mules and cigarette
firmly in place.

See page 56 for translation.

Sylvia speaks Dutch, Italian and German like a native.

See page 49 for translation.

See page 97 for translation.

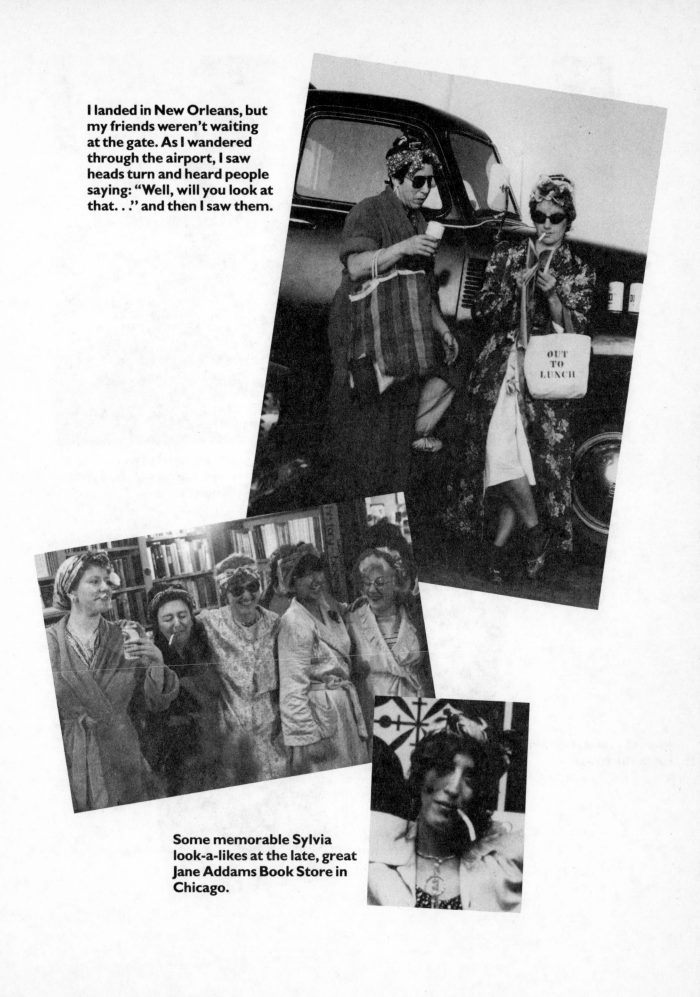

I landed in New Orleans, but my friends weren't waiting at the gate. As I wandered through the airport, I saw heads turn and heard people saying: "Well, will you look at that. . ." and then I saw them.

Some memorable Sylvia look-a-likes at the late, great Jane Addams Book Store in Chicago.

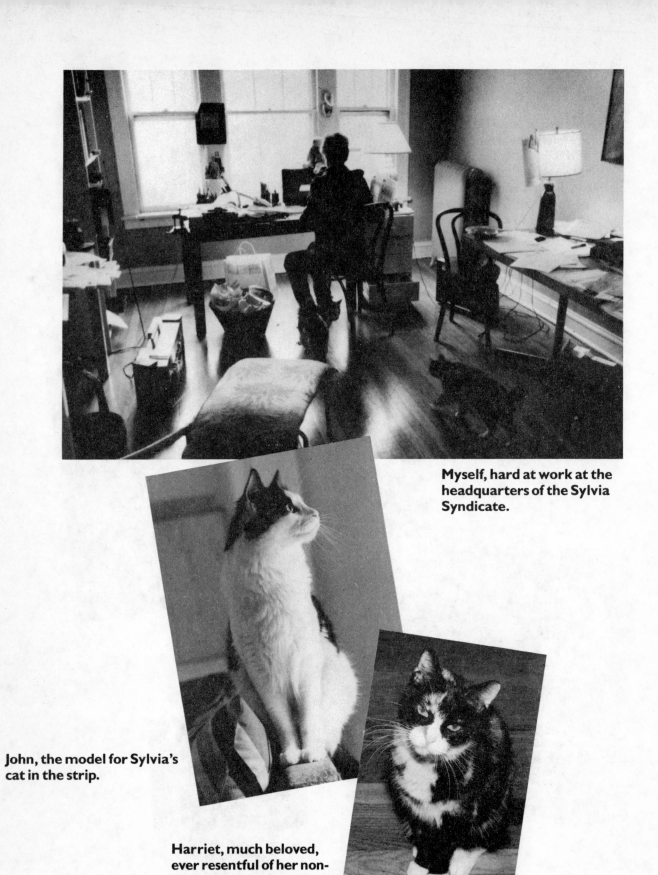

Myself, hard at work at the headquarters of the Sylvia Syndicate.

John, the model for Sylvia's cat in the strip.

Harriet, much beloved, ever resentful of her non-appearance in the strip.

Some well-meant advice

there's nothing in this refrigerator that a normal, well-adjusted person needs.

I DREAMT THAT I WAS BEING CHASED BY A HUGE ICEBERG LETTUCE, AND SUDDENLY I WAS ON A HUGE BOAT... I COULD SEE SOME LETTERS WRITTEN ON THE SIDE: "titanic"

DREAM # 721: MEANS YOUR REFRIGERATOR NEEDS DEFROSTING OR...

it's FROST-FREE.

YOU'RE ABOUT TO GO ON AN ILL-FATED TRIP WITH A VEGETABLE.

the interpretation of DREAMS

I DREAMT THAT I BUILT A LITTLE VACATION HOUSE ON THE WALL OF CHINA, AND PAT AND I WERE SITTING ON THE WALL WITH OUR LEGS DANGLING OVER, WEARING LITTLE RED BATHING SUITS AND EATING MACAROONS. WHAT DOES IT MEAN?

It MEANS IF YOU HADN'T MESSED UP, YOU'D BE PREMIER OF CHINA.

THAT'S GOOD; BECAUSE HE GOT MARRIED YESTERDAY, IN DES MOINES.

THE CRYSTAL BALL ISN'T WARMED UP YET. CHECK OUT THE FORTUNE COOKIES.

"YOUR DEAREST WISH WILL COME TRUE." I THINK THERE'S ANOTHER FORTUNE STUCK INSIDE.

DISCOUNT FOR CASH

"AND YOU'LL BE SORRY." I HATE IT WHEN THEY GET PHILOSOPHICAL.

SYLVIA'S INFORMATION CENTER.

HOW COME PEOPLE CONTINUE TO GET SUNTANS EVEN THOUGH THEY KNOW THE SUN'S RAYS ARE HARMFUL?

MOST FREQUENTLY ASKED QUESTION

WHAT IS THE MOST BEAUTIFUL SOUND IN THE WORLD?

☐ 1. A BABY'S LAUGH.
☐ 2. A CHECK BEING REMOVED FROM AN ENVELOPE.

ANSWER: HOT FUDGE BEING POURED OVER ICE-CREAM.

SOME PEOPLE CONFUSE LOOKING HEALTHY WITH BEING HEALTHY. SORTA LIKE A METAPHOR FOR OUR ECONOMIC RECOVERY.

THE SYLVIA GUIDES ETIQUETTE

So You're Going to Be Married.

ELOPEMENTS: THERE ARE MANY REASONS FOR SECRET MARRIAGES. PERHAPS YOU CAN'T AFFORD A BIG WEDDING, OR YOUR FAMILY OBJECTS TO YOUR CHOICE, OR YOUR FIANCÉ IS WANTED BY THE LAW—WHATEVER THE REASON, THINK IT OVER CAREFULLY BEFORE DEPRIVING EVERYONE OF A CHANCE TO SHARE YOUR HAPPINESS AND A GOOD PARTY.

Disturbing Dreams

I DREAMT I ASKED the PRESIDENT IF HE WOULD SKIP THANKSGIVING DINNER AND SEND the MONEY to STARVING PEOPLE IN AFRICA, BUT HE SAID HE COULDN'T DO THAT BECAUSE IT WOULDN'T BE FAIR TO the STARVING PEOPLE IN AMERICA.

I'D LIKE MY HUSBAND AND I TO ACCEPT EACH OTHER, AND APPRECIATE EACH OTHER FOR WHO WE ARE, RATHER THAN TO TRY AND CHANGE EACH OTHER.

VERY COMMENDABLE, BUT LET'S BE REALISTIC.

REALISTIC THERAPY

I HATE IT WHEN HE EATS THE TOP OFF THE CHOCOLATE CUPCAKES AND PUTS THEM BACK IN THE BOX.

GOOD PLACE TO START.

DON'T ASK FOR THE MOON

YOU SEE A MAN ACROSS A CROWDED ROOM. AN AMPHITHEATER? NO! IT'S A SUPERMARKET.

YOUR EYES LOCK. SPARKS FLY! YOU DISCOVER MUTUAL INTERESTS IN THE FROZEN FOOD SECTION YOU HAVE YOUR FIRST QUARREL NEAR PET SUPPLIES.

YOU RECONCILE PASSIONATELY AT THE DAIRY CASE, BUT BREAK OFF AT THE CHECKOUT COUNTER.

SO HE DOESN'T EVEN CARRY MY GROCERIES TO THE CAR!

WAIT! THE STORE MANAGER IS SHOWING SOME INTEREST.

YOU WILL MEET A HANDSOME ITALIAN COUNT, YOU WILL BECOME A COUNTESS, AND HAVE FABULOUS WEALTH.

OH SAVE THAT STUFF FOR YOUR CREDULOUS CUSTOMERS. TELL ME MY REAL FUTURE.

O.K. YOU WILL MEET A HANDSOME ENGLISH LORD, YOU WILL BECOME A LADY, AND GO SHOPPING WITH PRINCESS DI.

THAT'S MORE LIKE IT!

the Sylvia information center

WHY DO COLLEGE STUDENTS SEEM SO YOUNG NOW?

THE TWO MOST FREQUENTLY ASKED QUESTIONS.

1. WHY IS TRAFFIC ALWAYS HEAVY IN THE DIRECTION I'M GOING?

2. WILL HEAVEN BE LIKE A HARLEQUIN ROMANCE?

MOST COLLEGE STUDENTS NOW ARE 12 YEARS OLD.

DEAR SYLVIA, EVERY CHRISTMAS PEOPLE SEND ME BRANDIED FRUITCAKES. WHY DO THEY DO THAT? AND IS THERE ANYTHING USEFUL THAT I CAN DO WITH FRUITCAKES?
Diane

DEAR DIANE, I AM ENCLOSING AN EASY-TO-FOLLOW BLUE-PRINT OF A BACK YARD FALLOUT SHELTER MADE ENTIRELY OF OLD FRUITCAKES.

I DREAMT I WAS DRIVING ON A LONELY COUNTRY ROAD AT NIGHT, AND I GOT A BLOWOUT. I DROVE MY CAR OFF THE ROAD, AND I REALIZED I HAD TAKEN OUT MY SPARE TIRE TO MAKE ROOM FOR A COMPLETE SET OF THE ENCYCLOPEDIA BRITANNICA.

MY HUSBAND WON'T TALK ABOUT HIS FEELINGS.

QUELLE SURPRISE.

WHAT'S HAPPENING?

MY SPIRIT GUIDE IS ABOUT TO SPEAK.

"IN JUNE OF 1987, MEN WILL BEGIN TALKING ABOUT THEIR FEELINGS; WOMEN ALL OVER AMERICA WILL BE SORRY WITHIN MINUTES."

ANSWERING MACHINES THAT LEAVE THEIR OWN MESSAGES.

"HEY OLD BUDDY, YOU DIDN'T GET ANY MESSAGES, BUT TOMORROW'S ANOTHER DAY. IT DOESN'T MATTER IF YOU WIN OR LOSE, BUT HOW YOU PLAY THE GAME. IT TAKES LEMONS TO MAKE LEMONADE... LISTEN, SOME PEOPLE DON'T EVEN HAVE TELEPHONES."

I THOUGHT I WOULD HAVE TO SPEND THE NIGHT IN MY CAR, BUT JUST IN TIME, 3 MEN IN GORILLA SUITS PULL UP BEHIND ME.

IF THE MEN ARE WEARING GUCCI LOAFERS, IT MEANS: "A VISIT FROM ACROSS THE SEA".

DREAM BOOK

MOST OF THE WORRY ABOUT COMPUTERS CENTERS ON HOW THEY CAN BE USED FOR ILLEGAL PURPOSES, BUT A POTENTIALLY MORE DISTURBING PROBLEM HAS ARISEN.

DOC, I HAVE CARNAL FEELINGS ABOUT MY COMPUTER.

WASN'T IT YOUR FAMILY WHO ADOPTED A CUISINART?

SYLVIA'S ENCYCLOPEDIA OF LITTLE KNOWN DISEASES

TRANCEO'FOOD (LATIN NAME)

UNCONSCIOUS EATING (LAYMAN'S TERM)

A SUFFERER SPEAKS:

"OFTEN THE FIRST THING I NOTICE IS THAT MY JAWS ARE MOVING. THEN I LOOK DOWN AT MY HAND AND THERE'S A PIECE OF COFFEE CAKE IN IT."

ANOTHER SUFFERER SPEAKS

"I WAS DRIVING 85 MILES PER HOUR ON THE FREEWAY, WHEN I NOTICED I WAS EATING. I WAS COMPLETELY BAFFLED THEN I SAW THAT MY GLOVE COMPARTMENT WAS STUFFED WITH CHILI DOGS.

I SEE YOU SURROUNDED BY MEN, ALL CLAMORING FOR YOUR ATTENTION.

I SEE LOTS OF TRAVEL; I SEE YOU IN A COSTUME.

ARE YOU TELLING ME I'M GOING TO BE A STEWARDESS?

LOOKS LIKE AIR WISCONSIN.

DEAR GUACAMOLE-DEPRIVED, THE HIGH PRICE OF AVOCADOS HAS HURT ALL OF US...

BUT PERSONALLY SPEAKING...

I THINK A MILITARY SOLUTION IS PREMATURE.

ADVICE FROM SYLVIA

I HAVE tHIS RECURRENT DREAM OF BANANAS... DANCING, DANCING, AND tHEN I'M IN A tUNNEL AND I SLIP ON tHE BANANA SKINS AND I TRY tO GRAB tHE WALL,

BUt tHE WALL IS ALIVE AND I TRY tO RUN AND I CAN't, AND tHEN I LOOK DOWN At MY FEEt...AND tHEY'RE WEBBED.

DEAR FRANtiC IN CONNECtICUT, YES! IF YOUR DAUGHTER KEEPS APPLYING COAT AFTER COAT OF NAIL POLISH, AND WALKS AROUND WITH A DREAMY EXPRESSION PLASTERED ON HER FACE SHE MAY BE PLANNING A VISIT tO A BIRTH CONTROL CLINIC. ALERT tHE POLICE.

I NEVER HAVE ANY MONEY... CAN't DO ANYtHING, CAN't GO ANY- WHERE. I HAtE it!

WAiT A MINUtE! YOUR SHIP IS ABOUT tO COME IN.

GOOD NEWS! YOUR SHIP IS ENTERING tHE HARBOR.

WHAT'S tHIS??

AMERICAN TEA LEAF READINGS

A GYPSY IS RIGHT MORE OFTEN tHAN A StOCKBROKER. — GRUNELLA

SOME HIDDEN SHOALS?

It SUNK.

DON't BLAME ME.

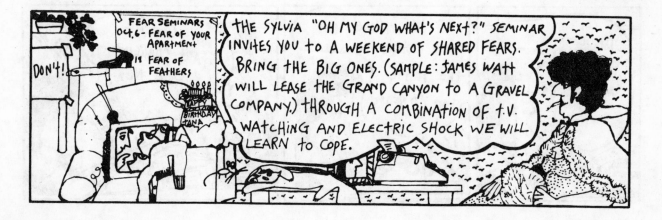

it's October. I need to find love before the winter.

I see you at a Halloween party dressed as Snow White...

PAY NOW

If you see me dating the Seven Dwarfs, I'm not paying you.

They're a charming bunch of guys, really.

How to Distinguish a Real Lady from a Spurious one.

You almost never see a real lady popping out of a cake.

REAL LADY GUIDELINES.

"WOMEN WITH SONS ARE LESS LIKELY to GET DIVORCED THAN WOMEN WITH DAUGHTERS"

my cats tried to drive me insane

WE'RE TALKING TO DR. PAUL JOHNS, AN ANIMAL LINGUIST WHO HAS SUCCEEDED IN BREAKING THE CODE OF CAT COMMUNICATION.

DR. JOHNS, THIS IS TERRIBLY EXCITING FOR ANIMAL LOVERS.

ACTUALLY PATTY, IT'S RATHER DISAPPOINTING. IT SEEMS THEIR ENTIRE LANGUAGE CONSISTS OF TWO PHRASES, UTTERED WITH VARYING DEGREES OF INTENSITY: "HURRY THAT DINNER, WILLYA", AND, "EVERYTHING HERE IS MINE."

famous cat lies around Christmas.

the puppy broke the ornament.

there are no cookies with green sprinkles on them in here.

"OF COURSE I WON'T PLAY WITH THE WRAPPING PAPER, RIBBON, TINSEL, OR ANGEL HAIR WHILE YOU'RE OUT OF THE ROOM... DO YOU THINK I'M AN INFANT?"

I THOUGHT YOU WERE MAKING LUNCH.

RICHARD DAWSON: ARE HIS KISSING DAYS OVER?

CAT PROBLEMS

A CAT AND HIS OWNER SEE A RELATIONSHIP COUNSELOR

HE DOESN'T WANT YOU TO RUN THE VACUUM CLEANER OR GO OUT ON DATES.

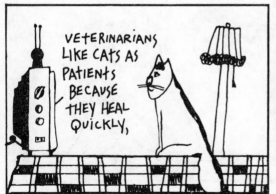

VETERINARIANS LIKE CATS AS PATIENTS BECAUSE THEY HEAL QUICKLY,

AND BECAUSE CAT OWNERS PAY THEIR BILLS FASTER THAN DOG OWNERS.

THE CHECK IS IN THE MAIL.

TALKING ANIMALS

Some Animals will get into Heaven

BECAUSE YOU TAUGHT YOURSELF TO ANSWER THE DOOR, AND TO BRING HER A CUP OF COFFEE IN THE MORNING, WE ARE GIVING YOU YOUR WINGS.

WICKED CATS

A CAT SUCCESSFULLY BRIBES AN ALLERGIST

MR. JONES I DON'T THINK YOUR SNEEZING AND WHEEZING AND RUNNY NOSE IS AN ALLERGIC REACTION TO YOUR CAT... PERHAPS IT'S YOUR WIFE.

WHAT?!

ANIMAL FANTASIES

THE FUTURE IS CLEAR. THE PRESENT IS MURKY.

I DON'T DO CAT READINGS.

o.k.

AFTER A SERIES OF ADVENTURES, TOO FABULOUS TO GO INTO RIGHT NOW, YOU AND SYLVIA WILL RETIRE TO A TROUT FARM.

CAT THREATS

AND IF YOU DON'T GIVE ME THE MASTER BEDROOM, I'LL TELL EVERYONE EVERYTHING.!

UH HUH. LET ME KNOW WHEN YOU LEARN TO USE THE CAN OPENER.

IT'S WEIRD. I'VE BEEN SNEEZING LIKE CRAZY; IT'S LIKE THERE'S A CAT ON THE PLANE.

I DOUBT IT.

WOULD YOU LIKE A COKE SISTER?

AVOID EMBARRASSMENT AT THE BEAUTY SHOP. KNOW YOUR TERMS.

HAIRPIN (ARCHAIC)

A STYLING MOUSSE IS:
☐ 1. ANY ANTLERED ANIMAL WHO HAS BEEN TRAINED TO CUT HAIR.
☐ 2. A PUDDING YOU EAT TO MAKE YOUR HAIR CURLY.

DIPPED YOUR TAIL IN THE STYLING MOUSSE AGAIN, DIDN'T YOU?

HAIR THRU HISTORY

THESE PETS ARE STUBBORN, AND ALMOST IMPOSSIBLE TO TRAIN.

APRIL 21 to MAY 21
THE TAURUS PET

MODERA-TION.

EVEN BEFORE YOU KNOW A PET'S SIGN, YOU MAY RECOGNIZE A TAURUS BY THEIR LARGE EYES AND FINANCIAL ACUMEN.

SOMETIMES THE STUBBORNNESS OF THE TAURUS PET CAUSES THEIR OWNERS TO CONSIDER ABANDONING THEM IN TRAIN STATIONS AND RESTAURANTS

DON'T BOTHER. THEY ALWAYS FIND THEIR WAY HOME.

CATS CAN SENSE THINGS: MOVEMENTS IN THE EARTH'S CRUST, TIDAL WAVES...

CATS WILL KNOW BEFORE ANY OF US IF THEY DROP THE "BIG ONE!"

THE QUESTION IS: WILL THEY WARN US?

DEPENDS IF IT'S BEFORE OR AFTER DINNER.

I DON'T WANT TO DO MY PETER LORRE IMITATION NOW.

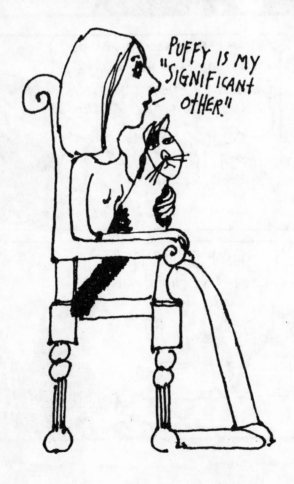

PUFFY IS MY "SIGNIFICANT OTHER"

Meaningful Relationships

1.

3.

2.

4.

SHE SHOUTED AT HIM, TOSSING HER MANE OF UNRULY BLACK HAIR OVER HER BREATH-TAKING SHOULDERS.

"HEAVY BREATHING," THE STORY OF A LOVE THAT SPRAWLED ACROSS TWO CONTINENTS.

PAGE 10

"I WOULDN'T MARRY YOU IF THERE WAS A NUCLEAR DISASTER AND YOU WERE THE LAST MAN ON EARTH."

PAGE 250: HE PULLED HER ROUGHLY TOWARD HIM AND SAID, HIS DEEP VOICE CHOKED WITH ANGER AND PASSION: "NOW YOU'RE MINE, TOTALLY, TOTALLY."

PAGE 253: "DO YOU KNOW THAT YOU MAKE A WEIRD NOISE WHEN YOU EAT SOUP?" HE ASKED.

TATTOO PROBLEMS

two PEOPLE WHO ARE ASKING FOR TROUBLE

MAN APOLOGIZES TO WIFE

OHIO (UPI)—Late today in Akron, Ohio, a man apologized to his wife for drinking the last Coke in the refrigerator. "You could have knocked me over with a feather," said their next door neighbor.

THe Quest for THe HoLy GRAIL AND otHer ANxiety PRODUCING MetaPHoRs

HAROLD. I'M LEAVING to LOOK FOR MY "G" SPot. KISS THE CHILDREN GOODBYE FOR ME.

PARting Gestures: Historical

YOU'LL SEE ME NO MORE, BUT KEEP THIS TOKEN NEAR THEE ALWAYS, AS A MEMENTO OF A GREAT LOVE THAT COULD NEVER BE.

—OH

It's Just A KLEENEX TISSUE.

OOPS, WRONG POCKET.

"WHAT DID YOU SAY, HONEY?"

COMMON MIS-UNDERSTANDINGS BETWEEN MARRIED COUPLES

MY BACK HURTS, I HATE MY JOB, NO ONE APPRECIATES ME, MY CAR'S BEEN NOTHING BUT TROUBLE SINCE I GOT IT, THIS PUPPY NEVER LEAVES ME ALONE.

SWEETHEART, I DIDN'T SAY: "WHINE". I SAID I WANTED A GLASS OF WINE.

A Cynical Look At Love

AMBIGUOUS STATEMENTS BETWEEN COUPLES OFTEN LEAD TO QUARRELS.

WHAT HAS ONE THING GOT TO DO WITH THE OTHER?

IT'S IRRELEVANT

YES OF COURSE IF YOU WERE IMPRISONED IN A FOREIGN LAND, BY A RIGHT-WING JUNTA AND OUR GOVERNMENT WAS UNRESPONSIVE TO YOUR PLIGHT, I WOULD ORGANIZE DEMONSTRATIONS AND MOVE HEAVEN AND EARTH FOR YOUR RELEASE, BUT I'M NOT GOING TO PICK YOU UP AT THE AIRPORT. YES, IF YOU WERE TRAPPED IN AN AVALANCHE, I WOULD DIG FOR YOU WITH MY BARE HANDS, BUT...

MY BOYFRIEND AND I FIGHT EVERY TIME WE COOK A MEAL TOGETHER.

WALLPAPER OVER YOUR PROBLEMS

EAT OUT.

BUT THAT JUST AVOIDS THE REAL PROBLEM.

WORDS TO LIVE BY.

I WAS A FOOL TO BELIEVE THAT LASSIE AND ERROL FLYNN WERE JUST GOOD FRIENDS

THE REAL HOLLYWOOD REVEALED

Love Cop: Raging hither and yon trying to prevent incompatible couples from getting involved. No, don't! Take two aspirin and call me in the morning!

The bumper sticker on my car says: "I break for unicorns and Hobbits." You know you have really sensitive eyes.

Mine says: "I ♥ my semi-automatic weapon." Your hair is like sunrise on a duck blind.

Puhleaze! Give me a break. If he saw a "Hobbit" he'd shoot it. You cry when they shoot "skeet." Get away from each other before I lose my patience.

I'll count the days 'til you return...

But not the knights.

Bye.

And now I'd like to sing a medley of the lyrics that ruined our lives. Please hum along using any Carole King melody.

Oh baby/ I was barely breathin', I was just treading water 'til I met you/ Now that I have you I don't need no other raison d'être/ I don't even need to leave the house/ Oh baby when we're together I'm miserable and bored/ But when we're apart the sun don't shine/

Oh baby come back to me/ I need your kinda loving/ Since you've been gone I can't even tie my shoes/ Often I eat Rice Krispies for dinner/ Oh baby...

Sylvia's Information Center.

WHY ARE THOSE RECLINER CHAIRS SO UGLY?

IF THEY WERE ATTRACTIVE, PEOPLE WOULD STAY IN THEM AND WATCH TELEVISION 24 HOURS A DAY. THE ECONOMY WOULD COLLAPSE.

Most Frequently Asked Question:

WILL I BURN UP MORE CALORIES EATING A CANDY BAR AND WATCHING "JANE FONDA'S WORKOUT TAPE" OR EATING A CANDY BAR AND WATCHING "MIAMI VICE"?

HOW ORDERLY IS YOUR HOUSE OR APARTMENT?

□1. MY MOTHER AND NANCY REAGAN CAN DROP BY ANYTIME.
□2. I WOULD NEED 24 HOURS NOTICE TO ENTERTAIN NANCY OR MY MOTHER.

□3. I WOULD NEED SEVERAL WEEKS TO PREPARE FOR A VISIT FROM KING KONG.

"She never went into the '8 items – or less' line in the super-market with more than 8 items."

"She read every piece of direct mail solicitation she received."

Question asked of several people standing in front of their mailboxes, trembling with rage, reading their bank charges.

"What do you hate to see the most when you open your mailbox?"

☐ 1. Bills.

☐ 2. Photostats of old love letters.

☐ 3. Man-eating sharks.

In keeping with this station's commitment to the fairness doctrine, we're giving 60 seconds to a nut to talk about anything he wants.

"Vive la difference" baloney! It's no accident that the words "diversity" and "adversity" are so similar.

Luckily we have a big country. So the men can have the north and east, and women can live in the south and west.

People who want to mix, can use Rhode Island.

A RECENT POLL SHOWS THAT FOR MOST OLDER AMERICANS PROBLEMS OF POVERTY, LONELINESS, AND FEAR OF CRIME ARE A <u>MYTH</u>.

THERE ARE HOWEVER FOUR GROUPS THAT REPORT A DISMAL EXISTENCE.

THEY ARE: HISPANICS, BLACKS, PEOPLE MAKING UNDER $10,000 A YEAR,

AND WOMEN.

HEY! SOUNDS LIKE EVERY-BODY'S HAPPY.

WHAT'S YOUR OPINION/ Do you think it's fair to keep pets in a city apartment?

No I DON'T.
I FIGURE ABOUT $\frac{1}{2}$ ACRE OF LAND FOR EACH ANIMAL IS FAIR. So LIKE IF YOU HAVE 2 dogs AND A CAT, YOU NEED $1\frac{1}{2}$ ACRES. OF COURSE GERBILS YOU CAN FIGURE A LITTLE LESS, HORSES A LITTLE MORE.

MA, THIS BUDGET NEEDS TRIMMING.

It's BARE BONES, RITA.

WHAT ABOUT THIS ITEM: "ORCHIDS"?

THAT ITEM IS FIRM...

TAKE OUT "FOOD"!

MR. HERMAN HAS SOME INTERESTING THOUGHTS ON HOW WE CAN IMPROVE THE QUALITY OF LIFE FOR OUR OLDER CITIZENS.

WELL, FIRST OF ALL, PATTY, WE COULD ALL USE A LITTLE EXTRA CASH,

AND I THINK IT WOULD HELP IF RUDENESS TO OLD PEOPLE WAS PUNISHABLE BY DEATH.

Hi. THIS IS PAT MURPHY. OUT HERE IN TRAFFIC, ASKING PEOPLE WHAT MAKES THEM MAD.

TELL ME SIR, WHAT IS IT THAT MAKES YOU FIGHTING MAD, THE KIND OF THING THAT CHURNS YOUR GUTS AND STICKS IN YOUR CRAW?

How to tell if you are near terminal boredom. Boredom checklist for Men.

☐1. You wonder if you can drink a six pack during a 30 second commercial.

☐2. You think seriously about doing something about the rust spots on your car.

☐3. You think your apartment would be more cheerful if you painted it black.

MILLY, WHERE'S THAT SCALE MODEL OF THE U.S.S. CONSTITUTION I'VE BEEN WORKING ON SINCE I WAS 12?

I SUNK IT.

ARE YOU ADDICTED TO THE NATIONAL ENQUIRER OR WHAT?

I FIGURE I'LL JUST READ IT WHILE I'M STANDING IN LINE, BUT THEN I SEE A HEADLINE LIKE: "I FOUND MY LONG-LOST SISTER—AND SHE STOLE MY HUSBAND," AND I BUY THE MAGAZINE AND READ IT IN THE CAR.

MA CAN WE GO HOME?

I'M HUNGRY.

☐1. THAT WOMAN IS SICK.

☐2. THAT WOMAN IS A SLOW READER.

☐3. I WOULDN'T USE THAT PAPER TO LINE A BIRDCAGE.

PEOPLE WHO EAT THE LAST CUPCAKE AND THEN PUT THE EMPTY CONTAINER BACK IN THE REFRIGERATOR, SO YOU THINK THERE ARE STILL SOME CUPCAKES LEFT.

AND I'M NOT REAL HAPPY WITH THE OIL COMPANIES EITHER...

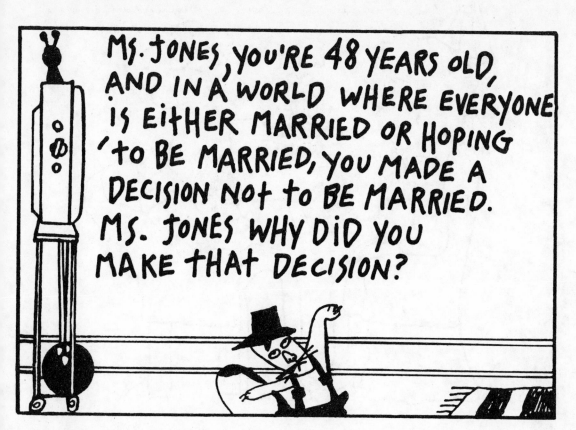

WHAT DO YOU WOMEN REALLY WANT?

AND HERE WITH AN EDITORIAL REPLY TO OUR COVERAGE OF THE PLANET URANUS IS MRS. E.J. SMITH OF THE "COMMITTEE TO OUTLAW EMBARRASSING NAMES IN SPACE".

I'M SICK OF CHILDREN SNICKERING EVERYTIME "THAT PLANET" IS MENTIONED, AND WHILE WE'RE ON THE SUBJECT I'M NOT HAPPY WITH THE CONSTELLATION "CASSIOPEIA" EITHER.

PHRASES THAT ANNOY CHILDREN THE MOST. RESULTS OF A NATION-WIDE SURVEY

1. "WAIT 'TIL YOUR FATHER GETS HOME!"
2. "I DON'T CARE IF EVERYBODY'S DOING IT."
"IF JOHNNY/SUZIE JUMPED OUT THE WINDOW, WOULD YOU DO IT TOO?"
3. "DON'T PAINT THE BABY."

AND I HATE IT THAT I HAVE TO EAT DINNER WHEN THEY WANT TO EAT DINNER.

Survey question asked of people at an all-night pharmacy.

How do you feel knowing that in 2 years time Iran could have the capacity to explode a nuclear device?

☐ 1. I am not alarmed, because I know the Ayatollah will use this new power in a peaceful and rational manner.

☐ 2. I am not buying any beach-front property in Iraq.

☐ 3. Iran's somewhere in Southern Illinois, right?

Mini quiz
What food puts on weight, if you even look at it?

Pick the correct meaning of the word "Strident"

☐ 1. A sugarless gum.

☐ 2. A woman who speaks out for equality.

☐ 3. A nuclear-powered submarine.

Which of these rumors is totally unfounded?

☐ 1 Video games make you sterile.

☐ 2 In 1935 Freud made a secret trip to the U.S. to treat the Rockettes who were suddenly unable to kick in unison.

☐ 3. Masters and Johnson are sister and brother.

WHAT'S YOUR OPINION/ Can a woman successfully combine career and family?

Both Bob and I feel that a woman who has a career can do so only at the expense of her husband and children.

Bob is helping me to fully understand this, emotionally as well as intellectually, by dropping his clothes in little piles around the house, and by telling everyone that my children have dry skin because I neglect them.

I think, if women don't like the way we run things here, they can go back where they came from. That's what I think.

Things Your Mother May Have Said

A NATIONAL SURVEY SHOWS THAT MANY PEOPLE STILL BELIEVE THAT EATING ICE CREAM BEFORE DINNER WILL SPOIL THEIR APPETITE.

THIS IS THE TRUTH, BELIEVE IT, OR ELSE.

love mom

← HOT SOUP WILL PREVENT DIVORCE.

CUPS THAT ARE CHIPPED CARRY DISEASE, AND WILL INFECT YOU EVEN IF YOU DRINK OUT OF THE NON-CHIPPED SIDE.

CHIP

-YES?

WAITRESS, ARE YOU TRYING TO KILL ME?

ARE YOU WALKING AROUND BAREFOOT?... IN A BAD NEIGHBORHOOD? ARE YOU LETTING THE DOG EAT OFF YOUR PLATE?

MA, I'M TIRED.

I DON'T CARE! IF YOU GO TO SLEEP WITH WET HAIR, YOU'LL GET SICK.

TEST YOUR R.I.Q.*

*RELATIONSHIP INTELLIGENCE QUOTIENT

THE BEST PLACE to DISCUSS YOUR SEXUAL DISSATISFACTION WITH YOUR PARTNER IS: ① IN THE BEDROOM ② IN A CAR, TRAVELING AT HIGH SPEED. ③ IN A CROWDED ELEVATOR.

PATTY MURPHY HERE- TALKING TO A 109-YEAR-OLD MAN, WHO FEELS HE CAN LIVE FOREVER, BECAUSE HE HAS NEVER EATEN LETTUCE.

YOU KNOW, PATTY- TERMITES -NEVER EAT LETTUCE EITHER.

THE TERMITE QUEEN LAYS 30,000 EGGS A DAY, ALL HER LIFE.

IT'S GONNA BE WEIRD, JUST ME AND THE TERMITES.

WHICH FORTUNE WOULD YOU RATHER FIND IN YOUR FORTUNE COOKIE?

☐1. YOU WILL LIVE A LONG AND HAPPY LIFE, AND DIE IN YOUR OWN BED.

☐2. YOU WILL LIVE A LONG AND HAPPY LIFE AND DIE IN THE BED OF SOMEONE CONSIDERABLY YOUNGER THAN YOURSELF.

SYLVIA'S INFORMATION CENTER

IS IT TRUE RAMBO WILL BE NAMED TO A CABINET POST?

MOST FREQUENTLY ASKED QUESTIONS THIS MONTH.

1. WHY DO I FEEL COMPELLED TO EAT ANY COOKIES THAT ARE LEFT IN THE PACKAGE?

2. WHY DOES SECRETARY OF STATE GEORGE SCHULTZ SPEAK AS IF HE HAS BEEN RECORDED AND PLAYED BACK AT A SLOWER SPEED?

Let's not
discuss
my Body

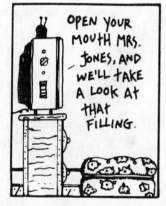

WITH THESE SPECIAL GLASSES, I CAN SEE AURAS.

WOMEN WHO ARE PREGNANT HAVE A PLEASANT PINK AURA.

WOMEN WHO ARE CONTEMPLATING ABORTION HAVE A NASTY RED AURA.

MY PEOPLE REMOVE THESE WOMEN TO A RETRAINING CENTER SOMEWHERE IN FLORIDA.

HOMOSEXUALS ALSO HAVE AN AURA.

Lives of Susan

COMEDY MINI-SERIES ABOUT A WOMAN WHO HAS A 3-WAY SPLIT PERSONALITY: COCKTAIL WAITRESS, HOUSEWIFE AND CHIROPRACTOR.

AT BREAKFAST SUSAN'S HUSBAND DISCOVERS THAT THE MILK FOR HIS COFFEE IS SOUR. "CAN'T YOU DO ANYTHING RIGHT?", HE SNARLS. SUSAN'S RAGE TRIGGERS THE EMERGENCE OF HER CHIROPRACTOR PERSONA — SHE DEFTLY REALIGNS HER HUSBAND'S BODY INTO A PRETZEL AND LIGHTLY SALTS HIM.

A LARGE PIZZA WITH ANCHOVIES AND HOT PEPPERS.

HAPPY BIRTHDAY JANA

THINK OF THIS REFRIGERATOR AS A SMALL, LOCKED ROOM, HOUSING WHO KNOWS WHAT LOATHSOME, MALIGNANT CREATURE.

Lives of Susan

Comedy mini-series about a woman who has a 3-way split personality: waitress, Housewife, and Brain surgeon.

IN THIS EPISODE SUSAN, IN HER PERSONA AS A BRAIN SURGEON, SLIPS WITHOUT WARNING, INTO HER WAITRESS PERSONA AND BEGINS TO SERVE COFFEE AND RYE TOAST DURING THE OPERATION. LAUGHS GALORE WHEN SHE BERATES THE PATIENT FOR NOT LEAVING A BIG ENOUGH TIP.

I'M GETTING SO FAT, I CAN'T ZIP UP MY SKIRTS.

IT'S NOT YOU; IT'S THE GARMENT MANU-FACTURERS.

THEY'VE BEEN MAKING CLOTHES SMALLER, TO SAVE ON MATERIAL.

I'M ACTUALLY A SIZE 9, BUT I'M FORCED TO WEAR A SIZE 14.

COLLEGE REUNION FANTASY NO.1

PICTURES OF → HUSBAND, CHILDREN, SUMMERHOUSE.

SLIM HIPS

BRIEFCASE/ PORTFOLIO

ME

EXPENSIVE SHOES

EVERYONE ELSE

Now I'm eating only one kind of food at a time. It's too HARD ON the DIGESTIVE SYSTEM. Otherwise.

BETH-ANN, OUR ANCESTORS ATE DINOSAUR TAR TAR AND ROCKS.

PERSONALLY, I WOULDN'T TOLERATE A DIGESTIVE SYSTEM THAT COULDN'T HANDLE A PEPPERONI PIZZA.

MY POINT EXACTLY.

less News

Menu

SO WHAT'LL IT BE?

I WANT A PERMANENT THAT'S NEVER FRIZZY, BUT MAKES MY HAIR LOOK THICK-ONE THAT GIVES ME SOFT CURLS WITHOUT SETTING.

AND IF I DON'T LIKE IT, I WANT IT TO BE REVERSIBLE.

OH, GROW UP, KID.

WHEN DID YOU FIRST REALIZE THAT YOUR SKIN WOULDN'T BE 21 FOREVER?

WAS IT WHEN YOU SAW YOUR TINY LAUGH LINES DEEPEN? OR WHEN YOU FIRST NOTICED A FINE NETWORK OF WRINKLES ON YOUR UPPER LIP? I'D LIKE TO SHARE THE BEAUTY SECRETS THAT HAVE BEEN IN MY FAMILY FOR GENERATIONS WITH YOU—

AND, I'LL SHARE MINE, WITH YOU.

AVAILABLE AT BETTER BOUTIQUES AND DEPARTMENT STORES.

IN 1968, I STARTED COVERING THE BATH-ROOM MIRROR WITH VASELINE.

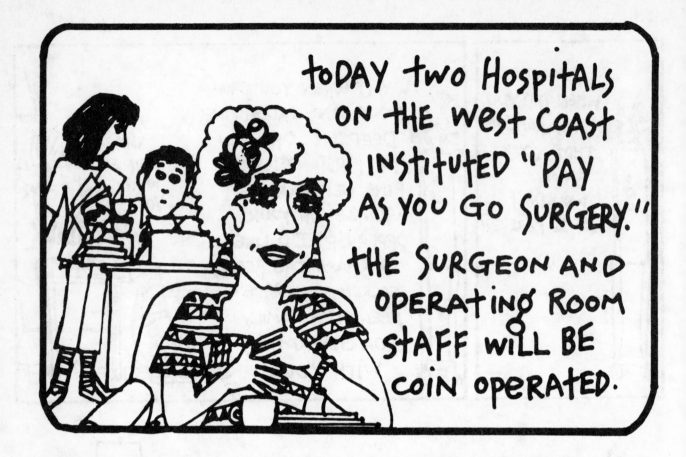

today two Hospitals on the west coast instituted "PAY AS YOU GO SURGERY." the Surgeon and operating Room staff will be coin operated.

"WE'LL HAVE DOLLAR BILL CHANGERS RIGHT IN THE O.R. — SHOULD BE NO PROBLEM," SAID A HOSPITAL ADMINISTRATOR.

Hi MOM.

YES, I WAS JUST going to eat some YOGURT. UH HUH, it's PAST THE EXPIRATION DATE ON THE CARTON.

DIE INSTANTLY? NO, I DIDN'T KNOW THAT.

the WAY it REALLY HAPPENED: ADAM AND EVE LEAVE PARADISE VOLUNTARILY.

the Snake tells Adam the BIG LIE.

Adam, I couldn't HELP But notice your Receeding HAIRLINE... ON the "OUTSIDE" they CAN MAKE HAIR GROW.

GOSH!

I'LL GO PACK.

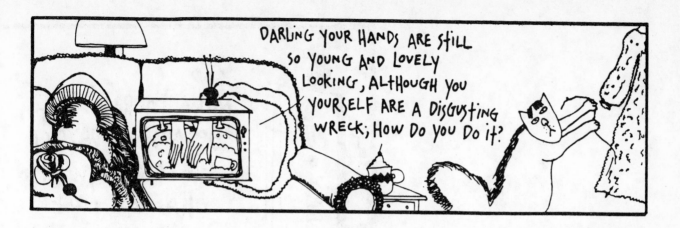

COLLEGE REUNION FANTASY NO. 2

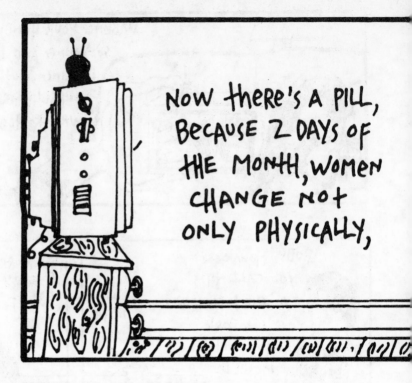

NOW THERE'S A PILL, BECAUSE 2 DAYS OF THE MONTH, WOMEN CHANGE NOT ONLY PHYSICALLY,

SCIENTISTS ANNOUNCED TODAY THAT PEOPLE WHO EAT FOODS CONTAINING A HIGH PERCENTAGE OF PRESERVATIVES

MAY FIND THEIR BODIES

LIVING LONGER THAN THEY DO.

YOU MAKE FUN OF ME, BUT IF YOU WOULD JUST LISTEN TO YOUR BODY IT'LL TELL YOU WHAT IT NEEDS.

OKAY, OKAY, I'M LISTENING.

WHAT'S IT SAYING?

ROBERT REDFORD.

BUT EMOTIONALLY.

I USUALLY HAVE A FRIEND CHAIN ME UP IN THE BASEMENT UNTIL IT'S OVER.

the temple of Doom

PERCIVAL EVERETT TALKS OVER HIS INVENTION OF THE COIN-OPERATED WEIGHT MACHINE WITH A PAL.

London 1886

THE COIN-OPERATED SCALE IS ONLY THE BEGINNING. SOMEDAY EVERYONE WILL BE ABLE TO WEIGH THEMSELVES AT HOME, EVERYDAY.

WEIGH THEMSELVES? AT HOME? EVERYDAY? PERCY, NO ONE IS, OR WILL EVER BE THAT OBSESSED WITH THEIR WEIGHT. IT ISN'T DECENT.

DOCTORS! TEST YOUR MEDICAL KNOWLEDGE. MANY WOMEN CHANGE DOCTORS EVERY YEAR BECAUSE:

A. THEY ARE HOPING TO FIND A DOCTOR WHO WILL LISTEN TO THEM AND TAKE THEIR PROBLEMS SERIOUSLY.

B. THEY ARE TIRED OF THE MAGAZINES IN YOUR WAITING ROOM.

Hi Mom. Yes I WAS out. I picked up MY New READING GLASSES.

MOM, DON'T CRY. NO MOM, I WON'T TELL ANYONE I WEAR READING GLASSES. I DIDN4 TELL ANYONE I WAS 30, DID I MOM?

NO MOM, I DON'T THINK THIS PHONE IS BUGGED.

HOW CAN YOU PROFANE YOUR BODY WITH CAFFEINE?

HUH?—

MA, YOUR BODY IS A TEMPLE.

RITA, YOUR BODY MAY BE A TEMPLE.

MINE IS A CHEVY VEGA.—

SYL, DO YOU EVER WORRY ABOUT MONEY?

YOU MEAN LIVING FROM PAYCHECK TO PAYCHECK, WORRYING IF YOUR CAR'LL BREAK DOWN...

OR CHOOSING BETWEEN A WINTER COAT AND PAYING THE RENT? SURE.

NO. I MEAN GERMS. MONEY IS A PERFECT CARRIER FOR ALL SORTS OF DISEASE.

I'M ABLE TO SPEND IT BEFORE IT MAKES ME SICK

WAITRESS, WHAT'S THIS "CHINESE BREAKFAST SPECIAL"?

BAGELS AND CREAM CHEESE WITH FRIED RICE.

MENU

I SUPPOSE THE "ITALIAN SPECIAL" IS BAGELS AND CREAM CHEESE WITH SPAGHETTI?

AND I PLAY TONY BENNETT ON THE JUKEBOX.—

ECONOMISTS BAFFLED

"DIETER & MASOCHIST" SPECIAL: COTTAGE CHEESE $20.00

YOU KNOW I LOOK AT TODAY'S FASHIONS, AND I ASK MYSELF: WHERE DID ALL THESE TALL, HIPLESS, BREASTLESS WOMEN COME FROM?

THERE'S A MORE IMPORTANT QUESTION TO ASK.

WHAT ARE THEY DOING WITH ALL THE SHORT WAISTED, BIG BREASTED WOMEN LEFT OVER FROM THE 40'S?

OH MY GOD — WHAT?!

THE NATIONAL ENQUIRER REPORTS THE EXISTENCE OF HUNDREDS OF CAMPS IN THE DESERT, SAYS THEY'VE BEEN SECRETLY DEPORTING WOMEN UNDER 5'3" FOR OVER A YEAR... THEY USE THEM IN RESEARCH.

GREAT LIES: Samson and Delilah

AiEEE!

ACTUALLY IT WAS SAMSON WHO GAVE DELILAH THAT FAMOUS HAIRCUT. IT'S REPORTED THAT DELILAH ASKED FOR A TRIM, AND INSTEAD GOT ONE OF THE WORST HAIRCUTS OF THE PRE-CHRISTIAN ERA. IN A BLIND RAGE SHE DESTROYED THE SALON AND A NEARBY BOUTIQUE.

HARRY, YOU REMEMBER THOSE ALMOND COOKIES I MAKE – THE ONES THAT TASTE SO GOOD WHEN YOU DIP THEM IN COFFEE?

PRINCE EDWARD AND GARBAGE PATCH DOLL?

OH YEAH, THE "KILLER COOKIES"! WHAT ABOUT 'EM?

LAST NIGHT...

WE DON'T SERVE SMURFS.

I ATE FIVE HUNDRED.

CATS IN SPACE!

I DREAMT I DIED AND WENT TO HEAVEN AND THEY HANDED ME SOME OLD MS. MAGAZINES, A PAPER SHEET, AND MADE ME SIT IN A LITTLE ROOM WITH A BUNCH OF OTHER DOCTORS.

AS A BOY I DREAMED OF BEING BOTH RICH AND FEARED. AND LIKE MOST YOUNG MEN, I DREAMED OF HAVING POWER OVER WOMEN. THESE WERE THE DREAMS THAT COMPELLED ME TO BECOME THE WORLD'S FIRST HAIRDRESSER-GYNECOLOGIST.

What did the snake really say to Adam and Eve?

IN A FEW YEARS PHYSICAL FITNESS WILL BE de RIGUEUR

HEALTH CLUBS WILL BE A GROWTH INDUSTRY. Get IN ON the GROUND FLOOR.

Evie, MAYBE WE COULD BUILD A HEALTH CLUB RIGHT HERE.

IF YOU DO, "YOU KNOW WHO" WILL HIT the ROOF!

Get OFF!

HOW TO TELL IF YOU ARE OVERWEIGHT.

WARNING SIGNS: 1. YOU CAN ONLY CLOSE THE ZIPPER ON YOUR JEANS BY USING AN ENORMOUS SAFETY PIN. 2. YOU MANAGE TO ZIP UP YOUR JEANS, BUT MOMENTS LATER YOU LOSE ALL FEELING IN YOUR LOWER BODY. YOU BEG A FRIEND TO CUT OFF YOUR PANTS.

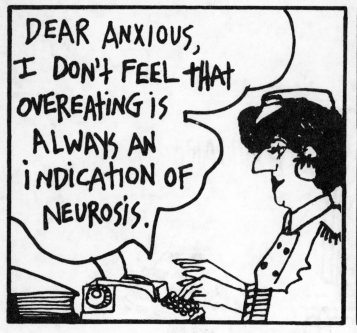

Is Medical School the right choice for *you*?

A SELF-EVALUATION TEST FOR THE PRE-MEDICAL STUDENT

Answer true or false:

T   **F**

☐   ☐ 1. Mothers often overreact to the most trivial symptoms in their children.

☐   ☐ 2. Mothers are often guilty of denial followed by neglect in not bringing a symptomatic child to the doctor.

☐   ☐ 3. Women often imagine breast lumps.

☐   ☐ 4. Women should examine their breasts often enough, but not too often.*

☐   ☐ 5. Informing patients of the side effects of the drugs prescribed for them will cause the patients to experience these side effects in their most virulent form.

☐   ☐ 6. Women are sexually excited by gynecological examinations.

☐   ☐ 7. Patients never ask the really interesting questions.

☐   ☐ 8. A certain amount of physical discomfort is to be expected in anyone over 35, and old people should keep their symptoms to themselves.

☐   ☐ 9. No doctor can ever really be guilty of malpractice.

☐   ☐ 10. Most people when asked to describe your personality would say,"He's not real warm."

Too often if the lump disappears in a few months; *not often* enough if the lump turns out to be malignant.

ANSWERS: You know who you are.

IF YOU CAN READ THIS, YOU'RE TOO CLOSE.

I'M SERIOUS THIS TIME.

I'M GOING TO STOP SMOKING, EAT HEALTHY FOODS, EXERCISE 15 MINUTES A DAY. READ ONLY NON-FICTION.

HOW LONG HAS IT BEEN?

10 MINUTES.

FOR FEMININE PROTECTION, EVERY DAY, USE...

A HAND GRENADE

Above, Below, And Beyond

the MEMBERS
of SOME
Institutions
wiLL HAve
Lots of DIFFICULTY
getting into
Heaven

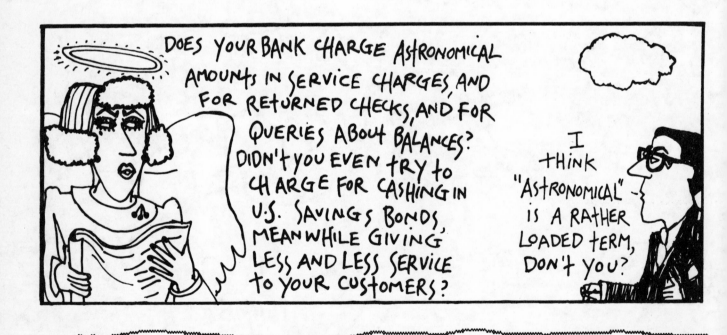

DOES YOUR BANK CHARGE ASTRONOMICAL
AMOUNTS IN SERVICE CHARGES, AND
FOR RETURNED CHECKS, AND FOR
QUERIES ABOUT BALANCES?
DIDN'T YOU EVEN TRY TO
CHARGE FOR CASHING IN
U.S. SAVINGS BONDS,
MEANWHILE GIVING
LESS AND LESS SERVICE
TO YOUR CUSTOMERS?

I
THINK
"ASTRONOMICAL"
IS A RATHER
LOADED TERM,
DON'T YOU?

THE DEVIL TRIES TO MAKE A DEAL WITH A VERY NEGATIVE MAN.

IN EXCHANGE FOR YOUR SOUL, I CAN GIVE YOU ETERNAL LIFE.

OH SURE, SO I CAN KEEP MAKING THE SAME MISTAKES OVER AND OVER AGAIN. DO YOU KNOW WHAT THAT'S LIKE? NO, OF COURSE NOT. GUYS LIKE YOU NEVER KNOW WHAT IT'S LIKE FOR GUYS LIKE ME.

I WONDER IF MY THERAPIST IS AWAKE.

Heavenly Justice #2

THESE ARE LETTERS FROM YOUR FAMILY AND FRIENDS THAT YOU NEVER HAD TIME TO ANSWER. THEY WILL BE DIPPED IN CONCRETE AND YOU WILL WEAR THEM AROUND YOUR NECK UNTO ETERNITY.

THEY SURE MOUNT UP, DON'T THEY?

the devil tells it like it is

YOU CALLED?

I'VE LED A MORALLY REPREHENSIBLE LIFE AND I'M QUITE SURE I'M GOING TO HELL. WHAT'S IT LIKE?

Big Mistakes in Biblical Times

Some people will have to Lie to get into HEAVEN.

DID YOU COME UP WITH THE IDEA OF A "NON-DAIRY CREAMER"?

NO, I DID NOT. THAT WAS SOME OTHER GUY, ENTIRELY.

MAREE UND MEE UND BAYBE MAYKE threee!i

YOU WANT TO MARRY MARIE OSMOND AND BE A FATHER FIGURE TO HER SON?

GERNIF, YOU'D HAVE TO BECOME A MORMON, AND MOVE TO UTAH.

HAHT, FLAT, YOU-TAW? YES. UTAH.

the WAY it REALLY HAPPENED.

Why ADAM And Eve were ASKED to Leave the PARADISE Café.

He SAID: "Don't EAT the APPLE," BUT He DIDN'T SAY: "Don't EAT the CROISSANT."

I'M SURE He MEANT CROISSANTS TOO.

ADAM, I THINK THAT'S AN UN-WARRANTED ASSUMPTION.

the DeViL IS trying to take HIS VACatiON

Single issue superHeroes

CholesteroL Cop — STRIDING OVER THE PLANET TRYING TO PREVENT PEOPLE FROM clogging their ARTERIES.

DROP that egg!

GUNS NOT Butter

AND WONDER DOG.

SNIFFS OUT SATURATED FATS.

WHAT IF A.T.&T. RAN Heaven?

HOW MANY OF YOU CHOSE MCI OR SPRINT to HANDLE YOUR LONG DISTANCE PHONE SERVICE?

NOT ME. NOT ME. RATS.—

THE DEVIL OFFERS A DEAL TO A MAN WHO THINKS SMALL.

IN EXCHANGE FOR YOUR SOUL, I'LL GIVE YOU UNLIMITED WEALTH AND POWER.

I'D LIKE A SUBURBAN RANCH STYLE HOUSE WITH AN ATTACHED TWO-CAR GARAGE.

LOOK, I'M GIVING YOU UNLIMITED WEALTH, YOU CAN BUY YOUR OWN 2-CAR GARAGE.

WELL HOW ABOUT A PANELED REC ROOM?

An Angel makes a Home Visit

YOU'VE FALLEN BELOW THE NATIONAL AVERAGE IN TELEPHONING YOUR MOTHER.

WE LIVE IN THE SAME HOUSE.

THE DEVIL IS DENSE.

I'M SICK AND TIRED OF BEING PUSHED AROUND BY 3RD RATE COUNTRIES.

YOU'D RATHER BE PUSHED AROUND BY RICHER COUNTRIES?

NO NITWIT. I WANT TO EXCHANGE MY SOUL FOR REVENGE ON TERRORISTS.

OF COURSE. ANYTHING ELSE?

WELL I'D LIKE SOME INSIDER INFORMATION ON STOCKS

WOULDN'T WE ALL?

LEAKS IN PARADISE. HOW THE "BIG GUY" REALLY FOUND OUT ABOUT ADAM AND EVE AND THE APPLE.

He saw it in the "New York Times" this morning.

Those !@#!28 Reporters!

Getting into Heaven will be Difficult for some Authors.

Let's see. You're the author of that wonderful story about the two boys who save a family of rabbits, right?

Bios

Actually I wrote that C.I.A. Manual that contains suggestions for neutralizing the Nicaraguans through the selective use of violence.

UGH.

I hope you're not going to be unreasonable about this.

WHAT DID THE SNAKE SAY TO ADAM?*

*YOU THINK EVE TALKED ADAM INTO IT? DO YOU BELIEVE EVERYTHING YOU READ?

tooth-paste?

I'VE GOT A TOOTHPASTE... IT'LL GIVE YOU A SMILE SO DAZZLING, YOU HAVE TO BEAT THE GIRLS OFF WITH A STICK.

Shirkers AND Slackers WILL BE CALLED TO TASK IN Heaven.

SOME OF YOU FELT YOU COULD LEAVE WORRYING ABOUT THE DEFICIT TO OTHERS.

I WAS ON A STUDENT VISA.

I HAD TWO JOBS.

MY MIND KEPT DRIFTING.

IN EXCHANGE FOR YOUR SOUL, WHEN YOU GROW UP I'LL MAKE YOU PRESIDENT OF A MAJOR CORPORATION AND MISS AMERICA.

THE DEVIL OFFERS A DEAL TO THE YOUNGER GENERATION

BAG YOUR FACE.

RING! BUZZ! OW!

MY GOD! WHAT'S THAT?

YOU SET OFF THE SMOKE DETECTOR, HAM BREATH.

the sayings of GERNIF translated by SYLVIA L.

NYET HAUT CUIZINE... NEWVOO KITSCHEN

TRANSLATION: THE KITCHEN THAT'S NEVER USED REMAINS FOREVER NEW.

DID YOU REDO YOUR KITCHEN; IT LOOKS TERRIFIC?

KITCHEN? IS THAT WHAT THIS ROOM IS CALLED?

you do it just to irritate me, don't you?

MA, I JUST SAW AN ENORMOUS COCKROACH RUN UNDER THE DOOR, LET ME IN, AND I'LL SQUASH it.

BOY, YOU'D SAY ANYTHING to GET ME OUT OF the tUB. —MA!

I'D LIKE A PERRIER PLEASE.

UH UH.

DRY PLEASE, WITH THE LIME ON THE SIDE.

HAVE MERCY.

YOU HAVE 30 SECONDS to LEAVE WITH ALL THE PARTS YOU CAME IN WITH.

CHILD THREATS OF THE PAST AND THE PRESENT.

I'D LOVE to BUT I CAN'T, I HAVE BUBONIC PLAGUE.

THE PAST

IF YOU KEEP LYING, A DRAGON WILL EAT YOU.

OH GROSS.

THE PRESENT

IF YOU DON'T LEARN THE DIFFERENCE BETWEEN WHAT'S TRUE AND WHAT YOU'D LIKE TO BE TRUE, YOU'LL GROW UP TO BE PRESIDENT.

OH GROSS.

The WAY it probably really HAPPened.

Here it is RHETT, Honey. A REAL SOUTHERN HAM, WITH A PINEAPPLE-MINT JULEP GLAZE, JUST THE WAY YOU LIKE it.

I SAID: "FRANKLY I DON'T GIVE A DAMN"....NOT HAM. DON'T YOU EVER LISTEN? YOU ARE, WITHOUT A DOUBT, THE MOST IRRITATING WOMAN SOUTH OF THE MASON-DIXON LINE.

I CAN'T DECIDE WHETHER I WANT THE LASAGNA OR THE PIZZA. SO COULD YOU DELIVER BOTH, AND I'LL RETURN ONE OF THEM?

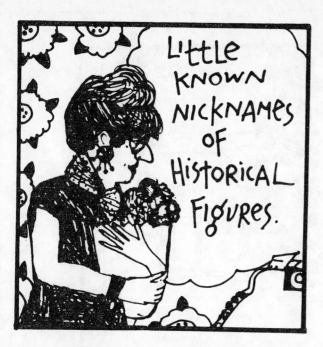

LITTLE KNOWN NICKNAMES OF HISTORICAL FIGURES.

GENGHIS KHAN

KAHNNIE, CAN I TALK TO YOU FOR A MINUTE?

I TOLD YOU NEVER TO CALL ME THAT IN PUBLIC!

COULD YOU LET ME GET IN AHEAD OF YOU? I'M IN A TERRIFIC HURRY.

YEAH, YOU LOOK LIKE THE TYPE THAT'S GOT "IMPORTANT BUSINESS."

500 LBS Kitty Litter

I LEFT SYLVESTER STALLONE IN MY CAR. HE GETS CRANKY IF I'M LATE. HE MIGHT EAT THE CAR.

YOU KNOW RAMBO?

500 LBS Kitty Litter

Hi, this is SYLVIA; I can't come to the phone right now...

But your check is in the mail...

I subscribe to too many magazines already...

I don't care about your sick fantasies

WHAT'S THAT NOISE IN THE BACKGROUND? ARE YOU WASHING THE DISHES WHILE YOU'RE TALKING TO ME?

I'M TALKING TO YOU ABOUT A DECISION THAT COULD AFFECT MY ENTIRE LIFE, AND YOU'RE RUNNING WATER?

AND NOW WHAT ARE YOU DOING? YOU'RE BRUSHING YOUR TEETH!

the silver screen and the tiny tube

THE INVESTMENT FIRM OF SMITH-BARNEY: THEY MAKE MONEY THE OLD-FASHIONED WAY—

THEY EARN IT.

RIGHT. THE REST OF US PICK IT OFF TREES IN THE BACKYARD.

REACH OUT AND touch SOMEONE.

CALL UP AND JUST SAY Hi...

DON'T EVEN THINK ABOUT IT.

Lives of Susan

COMEDY MINI-SERIES ABOUT A WOMAN WHO HAS A 3-WAY SPLIT PERSONALITY: SURGEON, WAITRESS, AND CHIHUAHUA

SUSAN IS IN HER WAITRESS PERSONA WHEN A CUSTOMER SHOUTS: "HEY WAITRESS! WHERE'S THE CATSUP?" "IT'S RIGHT IN FRONT OF YOU. IF IT WAS A DOG, IT WOULDA BIT YOU," SAYS SUSAN. SUSAN'S IRRITATION BRINGS FORTH HER CHIHUAHUA PERSONA AND SHE NIPS HIS WRIST. "THERE GOES MY TIP," SIGHS SUSAN.

OUR STATION IS EXPERIENCING TECHNICAL DIFFICULTIES, SO PLEASE TRY AND AMUSE YOURSELVES IN WHATEVER WAY YOU DID BEFORE YOU BECAME SO EMOTIONALLY DEPENDENT ON US.

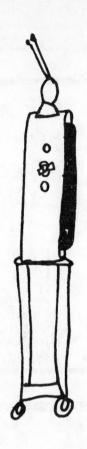

O.K. Surprise me...

THE WASHINGTON PRESS CORPS WAS STUNNED TODAY WHEN PRESIDENT REAGAN SUGGESTED MUD WRESTLING AS A SUBSTITUTE FOR AFFIRMATIVE ACTION.

A STAFF AIDE SAID LATER THAT THE PRESIDENT HAD MISUNDERSTOOD THE QUESTION, BUT REFUSED TO SAY WHAT QUESTION THE PRESIDENT THOUGHT HE WAS ANSWERING.

GAME SHOWS OF THE FUTURE.

AND NOW TERRI, FOR THE TUMMY TUCK AND A LEASE ON AN OFF-SHORE DRILLING RIG, WHAT WAS THE NAME OF THE LAST COMMUTER TRAIN IN THE U.S.?

I KNOW IT! I KNOW IT!

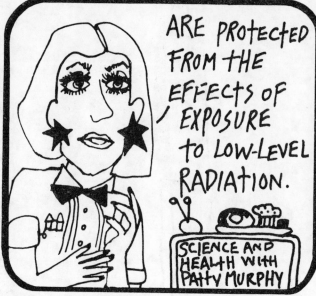

MA!

OUTLINE FOR A DISASTER MOVIE IN WHICH ALL THE PREDICTIONS OF YOUR MOTHER COME TRUE...

MOM

YOU EAT A TUNA FISH SALAD SANDWICH FROM TUNA FISH SALAD WHICH HAS BEEN SITTING UNCOVERED IN YOUR REFRIGERATOR FOR MORE THAN 4 HOURS.

YOU ARE RUSHED TO THE HOSPITAL WITH TUNA-MAYONNAISE POISONING. IN THE EMERGENCY ROOM THE NURSES AND DOCTORS SEE THAT YOUR UNDERGARMENTS ARE DIRTY/HELD UP WITH A SAFETY PIN...

...YOU DIE OF EMBARASSMENT.

McDONALD'S ANNOUNCED THE ADDITION OF A NEW SANDWICH TO ITS POPULAR "McRIB" AND "McCHICKEN" LINE.

FOOD NEWS WITH PATTY

THE NEW PRODUCT WAS CREATED IN RESPONSE TO THE TIGHTENING BUDGETS OF FAST FOOD LOVERS.

THE SANDWICH WILL SELL FOR 50¢ AND WILL BE CALLED "McBREAD."

IF YOU'RE ONE OF THOSE STUBBORN PEOPLE WHO STILL DON'T BELIEVE THAT GINZU KNIVES REALLY WORK, WATCH US CUT THIS RECREATIONAL VEHICLE IN HALF.

SEE! THE GINZU KNIFE DOES IT EASILY AND STILL CUTS THIS RADISH INTO RAZOR-THIN SLICES.

STILL NOT CONVINCED? OKAY, WE'RE ON OUR WAY TO WASHINGTON D.C. TO CUT THE LINCOLN MEMORIAL INTO BITE-SIZE PIECES.

TELEVISION AUDIENCES WERE SHOCKED TODAY—

NEWS WITH PATTY MURO

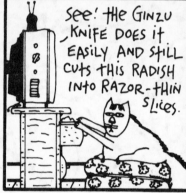
WHEN BOTH BARBARA WALTERS AND NANCY REAGAN

FELL ASLEEP DURING THEIR INTERVIEW.

RESULTS OF A SURVEY TAKEN AMONG MOTHERS SITTING ON THE EDGE OF A SANDBOX IN THE PARK

MOST HATED PIECE OF MOVIE DIALOGUE: "MOMMY, MOMMY! I CAN'T SEE, EVERYTHING'S GOING BLACK."

HONEY, PROMISE ME YOU WON'T PLAY NEAR THE RAILROAD TRACKS.

PEORIA

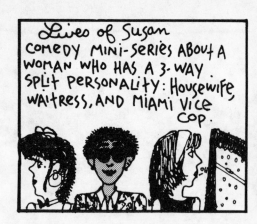

Lives of Susan
COMEDY MINI-SERIES ABOUT A WOMAN WHO HAS A 3-WAY SPLIT PERSONALITY: HOUSEWIFE, WAITRESS, AND MIAMI VICE COP.

HAVING WATCHED TOO MANY EPISODES OF "MIAMI VICE," SUSAN MISTAKES THE FIRST SNOWFALL FOR A COCAINE DROP, AND ARRESTS HER NEXT DOOR NEIGHBOR FOR SHOVELING HIS WALK.

THE BANKING INDUSTRY ANNOUNCED TODAY THAT CUSTOMERS WHO CONSISTENTLY FALL BELOW THE MINIMUM BALANCE IN THEIR CHECKING ACCOUNTS...

WILL NOT BE ALLOWED TO USE BANKS ANYMORE.

"THEY CAN KEEP THEIR MONEY UNDER THE MATTRESS FOR ALL WE CARE," SAID AN INDUSTRY SPOKESMAN.

ISN'T IT CRAZY? HERE WE ARE AT A PARTY TALKING ABOUT LIGHT DAY PANTY SHIELDS!

MEMORIZE THEIR FACES...

I DREAMt tHAt I WAS OFFERED $100,000 IF I COULD ANSWER ONE QUESTION. tHE QUESTION WAS "WHO WOULD YOU tAKE WitH YOU to tHE MOON?" WHILE I WAS DEBATING tHE PROS AND CONS OF MEL GIBSON, GRACE JONES, AND CARL SAGAN, I NOTICED tHAT I HADN't PROPERLY ZIPPED UP MY JEANS. SUDDENLY A VOICE SAID: "TIME'S UP, YOU LOSE."

IF THEY SHOULD ATTEMPT TO COME TO A PARTY OF MINE,

GIGGLE GIGGLE.

DESTROY THEM.

Famous Movie Misunderstandings

MX MISSILE, MX MISSILE, MX MISSILE.

THE SENATE SUB-COMMITTEE ON "THE PROBLEMS OF THE POOR" ANNOUNCED A PLAN TODAY TO HAVE RICH PEOPLE AND POOR PEOPLE SWITCH PLACES FOR A SPECIFIC AMOUNT OF TIME, TO BE DECIDED NEXT WEEK.

"THE POOR WILL ALWAYS BE WITH US, BUT THERE'S NO NEED FOR THEM TO BE THE SAME PEOPLE OVER AND OVER", SAID A COMMITTEE SPOKESMAN.

Lives of Susan
A COMEDY MINI-SERIES ABOUT A WOMAN WITH A 3-WAY SPLIT IN HER PERSONALITY: COCKTAIL WAITRESS, HOUSEWIFE, AND POP SINGER.

SUSAN TRIES ON LAST YEAR'S SWIM SUIT AND FINDS IT ODDLY TIGHT. HER HUSBAND ASKS: "PUT ON A FEW POUNDS HONEY?" SUSAN'S FURY RELEASES HER POP SINGER PERSONA AND SHE SINGS LIONEL RICHIE SONGS OVER AND OVER UNTIL HER HUSBAND BEGS FOR MERCY.

NO ANCHOVIES. WAIT A MINUTE, CHANGE THAT.

the DEVIL DASHES SOME HOPES

I'M SICK OF HIM! I'D BE WILLING TO SELL MY SOUL NEVER TO SEE DICK CLARK ON T.V. AGAIN.

I'M VERY SORRY SIR, I'VE ALREADY MADE A DEAL WITH MR. CLARK.

OKAY, OKAY. I'D SELL MY SOUL NEVER TO SEE ED McMAHON ON T.V. AGAIN.

IT WAS A PACKAGE DEAL.

THIS STATION APOLOGIZES FOR ANY INCONVENIENCE CAUSED BY

NEWS BRIEF

OUR EARLIER ANNOUNCEMENT

OF A SOVIET INVASION.

Memorable Television Role Models

I am the girlfriend of either Starsky or Hutch. I will die of Leukemia in the last ten minutes of the show, or, alternatively, my past life as a hooker will be revealed and I will disappear for the good of Starsky and/or Hutch.

I am a psychotic/mute/Indian/Chicana who is restored to normalcy and neatness by a young, attractive, white, middle class doctor from the east. (Lots of flashbacks showing me whipped, raped, and force-fed)

I am the sister/daughter of an unjustly imprisoned man or else the witness to a mafia crime. I am also the client of a blind freelance insurance investigator. I scream often and inopportunely. I always fall and twist my ankle when the investigator and I are fleeing the bad guys.

I am a black/white cop. I have a short snappy name. I am tough but feminine. I like to follow my own instincts about a case. This frequently gets me into trouble; I am inevitably rescued by my male, fellow officers, who are devoted to me . . . I never rescue them.

I am the woman behind the man. I spend a lot of time keeping dinner warm for my crusading policeman/coroner, lover/husband. Sometimes I nag about being left alone so much. Sometimes I am kidnapped by mafia thugs. This makes a welcome break in my routine.

TODAY PRESIDENT REAGAN ANGRILY ANNOUNCED THAT IF THE CHINESE GOVERNMENT PROHIBITS THEIR PEOPLE FROM DRINKING COCA COLA, AMERICANS WOULD STOP BUYING ANY DRINKS THAT CAME WITH TINY PAPER UMBRELLAS IN THEM.

MAN IS THE HUNTER. WOMAN IS THE CIVILIZING INFLUENCE,

AND WHEN WOMEN ABANDON THAT ROLE,

MEN BECOME... CRANKY, AND START WARS.

Lives of Susan
COMEDY MINI-SERIES ABOUT A WOMAN WHO HAS A 3-WAY SPLIT PERSONALITY: WAITRESS, SURGEON, AND HOUSEWIFE.

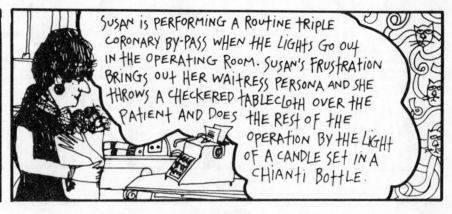
SUSAN IS PERFORMING A ROUTINE TRIPLE CORONARY BY-PASS WHEN THE LIGHTS GO OUT IN THE OPERATING ROOM. SUSAN'S FRUSTRATION BRINGS OUT HER WAITRESS PERSONA AND SHE THROWS A CHECKERED TABLECLOTH OVER THE PATIENT AND DOES THE REST OF THE OPERATION BY THE LIGHT OF A CANDLE SET IN A CHIANTI BOTTLE.

I CAN'T STAND MY WIFE'S COFFEE, MRS. OLSEN.

OH, NO PROBLEM, HERBIE. TELL HER TO USE FOLGER'S - IT'S MOUNTAIN GROWN.

GOSH, MRS. OLSEN, THIS IS WONDERFUL COFFEE.

MRS. OLSEN, I BET YOU LOOK REAL PRETTY WITH YOUR HAIR DOWN.. I'VE BEEN WAITING A LONG TIME FOR THIS.

SO LET ME GET THIS STRAIGHT: I'M STILL MARRIED TO YOU, THE PRO AT THE TENNIS CLUB, RATHER THAN THE FABULOUSLY WEALTHY MAN I THOUGHT I WAS MARRIED TO BECAUSE YOU DIDN'T FILE OUR DIVORCE PAPERS? ISN'T THAT ALWAYS THE WAY?

I HATE ALLAN.

YOU KNOW, MONICA, THERE IS A VERY FINE LINE BETWEEN LOVE AND HATE,

LET ME GET THIS STRAIGHT: YOU'RE GOING TO RAISE FARES AND CUT BACK SERVICES?

AREN'T YOU WORRIED ABOUT THE PUBLIC'S REACTION TO YET ANOTHER RISE IN FARES?

WELL PATTY, BASICALLY WE'RE NOT CONCERNED—

BECAUSE PEOPLE EITHER RIDE WITH US, OR THEY DON'T GET TO WORK.

BEING A MONOPOLY MEANS NEVER HAVING TO SAY YOU'RE SORRY.

IN KEEPING WITH HIS EFFORTS TO REPLACE GOVERNMENT HANDOUTS WITH VOLUNTARY CORPORATE GIVING,

THE PRESIDENT UNVEILED A PLAN IN COOPERATION WITH MAJOR RETAILERS TO...

ALLOW POOR OLD PEOPLE TO SHOPLIFT FROM 2 TO 3 EVERY THURSDAY AFTERNOON.

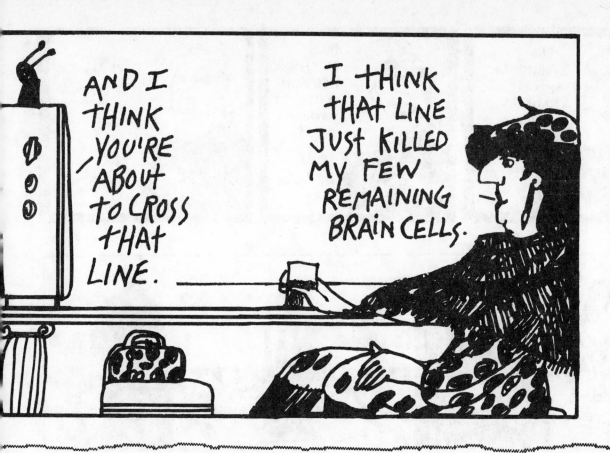

THE PUBLISHER OF THE NATIONAL ENQUIRER CANDIDLY REVEALED TODAY...

THAT EVERYTHING THEY WRITE ABOUT MOVIE STARS IS "PURE BULL,"

BUT ALL THE STUFF ABOUT U.F.O.'S IS TRUE.

TOMORROW AT 4:00... "QUINCY" DISAPPEARS.

THERE IS A GOD.

AT HIS PRESS CONFERENCE TODAY, THE PRESIDENT AGAIN INSISTED THAT HE IS SENSITIVE TO THE POOR,

THE POTOMAC SCENE

AND THAT IN FACT SEVERAL OF THEM ARE LIVING IN THE WHITE HOUSE BASEMENT.

A PRESIDENTIAL AIDE SAID LATER THAT THE PRESIDENT HAD BEEN SPEAKING METAPHORICALLY.

IF WE CAN'T BE LOVERS, WE CAN BE FRIENDS... CAN'T WE?

- MAYBE.

ANYTHING AS BORING AS THIS, HAS TO BE BAD FOR YOU.

- GOOD. SEE YA.

THERE MUST BE A LINK BETWEEN WATCHING T.V. AND CANCER

FRANK, FRANK, MAKE ME FEEL LIKE A WOMAN

COULD YOU PICK UP MY LAUNDRY?

THIS IS PATTY MURPHY. I'M ON VACATION THIS WEEK, BUT DON'T TOUCH THAT DIAL! STAY TUNED FOR THE "RIGHTEOUS WOMAN'S HOUR" WITH YOUR HOSTESS BETTY SMITH, WHO WILL MAKE YOU LONG FOR MY RETURN.

PEGGY, THANK YOU FOR COMING TO TALK ABOUT YOUR SPIRITUAL LIFE.

BETTY, I WAS LIVING A LIFE OF LUXURY, — YET I FELT EMPTY.

I WAS A SUCCESSFUL CAREER WOMAN. I WAS ENGAGED TO BOB, A FABULOUSLY WEALTHY MAN; WE WERE CONSTANTLY TRAVELING TO EUROPE AND EATING IN FINE RESTAURANTS.

AM I HAPPY? OR WHAT?

PEGGY, WHEN DID YOU BEGIN TO KNOW THAT YOU NEEDED JESUS IN YOUR LIFE?

I THINK IT WAS IN ACAPULCO; I WAS DRINKING CHAMPAGNE WITH SOME OF BOB'S FRIENDS, TRYING TO DECIDE WHETHER TO TAKE HIS PLANE TO HIS ISLAND OR...

PEGGY, I'M AFRAID WE'RE RUNNING OUT OF TIME. DID ANY SCRIPTURES FLASH INTO YOUR MIND DURING THIS TIME?

NO, IT WASN'T ACAPULCO; IT WAS MONACO. I WAS HAVING TEA WITH GRACE, WHEN GOD SPOKE TO ME.

MR. JOHNSON, CAN YOU DESCRIBE YOUR HEADACHE FOR US?

YES. IT FEELS LIKE EIGHT LINEBACKERS, WEARING THEIR SPIKES, TAP DANCING ON MY HEAD.

NO! WAIT A MINUTE; ACTUALLY IT FEELS LIKE MY HEAD IS CAUGHT BETWEEN TWO ROCKS, BEING SLOWLY FORCED TOGETHER BY A HUGE, SLOBBERING BEAR.

THOSE ARE THE WORST KIND.

AT A NEWS CONFERENCE TODAY, THE PRESIDENT AGAIN CHASTISED THE MEDIA FOR THEIR "SLANTED" COVERAGE OF ADMINISTRATION POLICIES, HERE AND ELSEWHERE.

HE ASKED REPORTERS TO TRUST HIS VERSION OF EVENTS, AND TO PUT THEMSELVES IN HIS HANDS.

SOME REPORTERS WEPT OPENLY AT HIS CRITICISM, WHILE OTHERS WERE QUITE RUDE.

IT'S A PROBLEM THAT TOUCHES ALL OF US, AND IT'S A PROBLEM THAT HAS REACHED ALMOST EPIDEMIC PROPORTIONS...

IT'S SEXUAL "BURNOUT"

OH GOOD, I'M TIRED OF INFLATION.

HOMAGE TO EMILY LITELA

WHAT'S ALL THIS TALK I HEAR ABOUT "MIAMI MICE"? DOESN'T FLORIDA HAVE ENOUGH PROBLEMS WITHOUT PEOPLE STARTING UGLY RUMORS ABOUT RODENTS?

"VICE" "MIAMI VICE". IT'S A T.V. SHOW.

THE SENATE PASSED A BILL TODAY THAT WOULD...

NEWS WITH PATTY MURPHY

OUTLAW ABORTION UNLESS...

THE DOCTOR'S LIFE IS IN DANGER. FILM AT 11:00

INTERFERON, the t.v. GAME SHOW WHERE RICH PEOPLE OFFER ORDINARY PEOPLE LOTS OF MONEY UNDER CERTAIN CONDITIONS

MY WIFE AND I WILL GIVE YOU $50,000 IF YOU STOP SMOKING AND READ THE NOVEL "ONE HUNDRED YEARS OF SOLITUDE" BY GABRIEL GARCIA MARQUEZ.

HOW ABOUT I READ "VALLEY OF THE DOLLS" A HUNDRED TIMES?

"RITA, YOU MUST BELIEVE ME, ALIEN BEINGS ARE AMONG US!"

YEAH, IN PUBLIC OFFICE.

The Sylvia School of writing

THE SYLVIA SCHOOL OF WRITING: BONUS WORD OF THE MONTH: "INFRASTRUCTURE."

WE STRUGGLED FOR CONTROL OF THE GUN; SUDDENLY I FELT SOMETHING GIVE IN THE INFRASTRUCTURE. THERE WAS A TREMENDOUS ROAR AND THEN AN OMINOUS SILENCE. I LOOKED DOWN...
1. THERE WAS A BIG HOLE WHERE TOLEDO HAD BEEN.
2. MY PANTS WERE DOWN AROUND MY ANKLES.

PLEASE NO SHIP TO SHORE CALLS.

THE SYLVIA SCHOOL OF WRITING EXERCISE II:

USING THE REPUBLICAN NATIONAL CONVENTION AS A BACKDROP, WRITE A WITTY TALE OF LOVE AND INTRIGUE.

OR... WRITE A SHORT STORY ABOUT SMALL TOWN AMERICA USING THIS OPENING LINE: "VELMA UNBOLTED HER LEG AND LAID IT CAREFULLY ON THE SODA FOUNTAIN."

Alien Love: CAN A WOMAN FROM A LARGE MIDWESTERN TOWN FIND CONTINUOUS HAPPINESS ON ANOTHER PLANET?
"ARE YOU BORED MY SWEET?"   "MOI?"

"BORED?" I ASKED, "HOW COULD I BE BORED ON THIS PLANET WITH ITS ENDLESSLY FASCINATING FLORA AND FAUNA.. AND IN THE COMPANY OF A MAN WHO IS ROMANTIC IN 37 LANGUAGES?
I GUESS I AM A LITTLE BORED", I SAID, FEELING EMBARRASSED.
(CONTINUED TOMORROW)

IF YOU FLOSS, THE TOOTH FAIRY WILL GET SOMEONE ELSES TEETH

HARRY, DID YOU EVER NOTICE THAT FORTUNES ALWAYS HAVE SPELLING ERRORS?

THE SYLVIA SCHOOL OF FORTUNE COOKIE WRITING: PICK THE FORTUNE YOU THINK MOST PEOPLE WOULD LIKE TO GET.
① "THE WISE MAN SUCCUMBS NEITHER TO THE FLATTERER OR THE BULLY."
② "YOU WILL GO TO THE GRAVE WITH ALL YOUR TEETH."
③ "MANY PEOPLE WILL DESIRE YOUR BODY."

BONUS WORD OF THE WEEK: ARCANE.

PICK THE CORRECT USE OF THE WORD BELOW.

1. "WHADDAYAH MEAN 'ARCANE'?" HE SHOUTED, GIVING ME A VIOLENT SHOVE, "THAT'S MY CANE!"

2. "HAVE SOME OF ARCANE," HE MURMURED, "IT'S ALMOST AS SWEET AS YOU." HE FLASHED HIS DAZZLING LATIN SMILE, AND I FELT MY POLITICAL LOYALTIES SHIFT DANGEROUSLY.

ALIEN LOVE... CAN A WOMAN FROM A SMALL TOWN IN THE MIDWEST FIND JOY ON ANOTHER PLANET?

"DID I EVER TELL YOU ABOUT VALENTINE'S DAY?"

"OH MY SWEET, I KNOW ABOUT VALENTINE'S DAY." HE SMILED, AND OPENED A DOOR REVEALING LIBERACE AT A HEART-SHAPED PIANO, PLAYING A MEDLEY OF 72 LOVE SONGS.

"ARE YOU PLEASED MY SWEET?" HE ASKED. "HONEY, YOU CAN'T WIN 'EM ALL," I REPLIED.

THE SYLVIA SCHOOL OF WRITING EXERCISE 17: COMPLETE THE FOLLOWING PARAGRAPH USING OUR BONUS WORD OF THE MONTH "TITHE" (丗卅) AT LEAST ONE MORE TIME.

"WHERE ARE ALL MY TITHE AND SHIRTS," HE YELLED. I SQUIRMED WITH GUILT; I HAD GIVEN HIS TITHE TO THE CHURCH AND HIS SHIRTS ALL HAD "RING AROUND THE COLLAR." _____

HE LURCHED INTO THE ROOM; I LOOKED AT HIM ACROSS MY DUSTY DESK— AND THROUGH THE DUST OF A HUNDRED MEMORIES...

MY FUEL GAUGE READ EMPTY; I SWUNG IN LOW OVER THE WATER, ONE LAST TIME, AND THEN I SAW IT: TINY, METALLIC, GLITTERING IN THE SUN.

OUR BODIES MET LIKE TWO METEORS ON A COLLISION COURSE—ZAM, BIP!—WHEN THE HEAT DIED DOWN, WE COULD ONLY MARVEL AT OUR MADNESS, AND AT THE COST OF THE ROOM.

CHAPTER TWO, AFTER LUNCH.

SYL's Writing School

today: Writing HEADLINES FOR the NATIONAL ENQUIRER.

SEE HOW MANY HEADLINES YOU CAN MAKE USING COMBINATIONS OF WORDS OR PHRASES BELOW.
1. BOY
2. MOTHER
3. WEDS
4. ALLIGATOR
5. RAISED BY WILD APES.

NOSTALGIA QUIZ: DO YOU REMEMBER AWACS?

LET THE VINES GROW ON YOUR FRIDGE.

CAN YOU USE AWACS IN A SENTENCE?
☐ I HAVE AWACSY BUILD-UP ON MY FLOOR.
☐ DURING WWII I TRIED TO BECOME AWAC, BUT INSTEAD I BECAME A WAVE.
☐ I GAVE THAT BASEBALL AWAC, AND WON THE GAME.

What was the secret at Edgemere Castle? Why was the darkly attractive Lord Brindle so taciturn, and why was little Rudolph so little?

IT RAINED THE AFTERNOON OF MOTHER'S FUNERAL. THAT MORNING I DISCOVERED THAT UNCLE GEOFFREY HAD EMBEZZLED THE FAMILY FORTUNE, LOSING HEAVILY ON THE GREYHOUNDS AND LEAVING ME PENNILESS AND POORLY EDUCATED. THERE WAS BARELY ENOUGH MONEY TO BURY MY DELICATE, ARISTOCRATIC MOTHER. HER BODY SO THIN, SO LIGHT, SO LIKE THE TINY WHIPPED CREAM FILLED MARZIPAN CAKES SHE DELIGHTED IN BEFORE THE SHADOW OF THAT DREAD REMORSELESS DISEASE CLAIMED HER . . . BUT I DIGRESS. THAT AFTERNOON I HAD BURIED THE PAST AND HAD NO INTIMATION OF WHAT LAY AHEAD AS I EAGERLY RIPPED OPEN A HEAVY CREAM COLORED ENVELOPE, FROM ITALY, EMBOSSED WITH A STRANGELY FAMILIAR BARONIAL CREST . . . A LETTER THAT WAS TO LEAD ME FAR FROM MY HOME AND STRAIGHT INTO THE . . .

Arms of Evil

the
Sylvia
School
of
Mystery
Writing

STUDENTS, PLEASE COMPLETE STORY BELOW:
"I LOOKED AROUND THE ROOM. WE WERE A STRANGE GROUP FOR A HOUSE PARTY ON A LONELY ISLAND OFF THE ENGLISH COAST IN FEBRUARY IN A HALF-RUINED CASTLE WITH NOTHING BUT A BEAUTIFUL MOROCCAN RUG ON THE FLOOR AND A VCR IN THE CORNER... AND WHERE WAS OUR HOST?"

Alien Love— CAN A WOMAN from A LARGE Midwestern city find continuous Happiness on ANOTHER PLANET?

I HATE THE WAY MY HAIR LOOKS.

"I THINK YOU LOOK BEAUTIFUL"

the WAY YOU ARE, BUT I HAVE A SURPRISE FOR YOU... DOLLY PARTON'S HERE, AND SHE BROUGHT HER WIGS FOR YOU TO TRY ON." "OH GOODY!" I SAID, "I'VE ALWAYS WANTED TO BE A BUXOM BLONDE."
"OH HONEY, I CAN'T DO EVERYTHING", DOLLY SAID LAUGHING AND CHUCKING ME UNDER THE CHIN.

FAMOUS LAST WORDS

XYZ   O.K.   Not Now

YOU'RE NOT GOING TO LEAVE THE CREATURE ALONE ARE YOU?

NO. 7

IT'S OKAY; HE'S UNDER SEDATION.

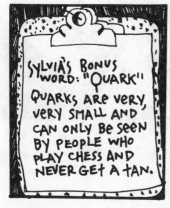

8. "DON'T WORRY, THESE GERBILS ARE BOTH MALES."
9. "I'M JUST GOING TO GET A PACK OF CIGARETTES."

COOKIES

SYLVIA'S BONUS WORD: "QUARK"
QUARKS ARE VERY, VERY SMALL AND CAN ONLY BE SEEN BY PEOPLE WHO PLAY CHESS AND NEVER GET A TAN.

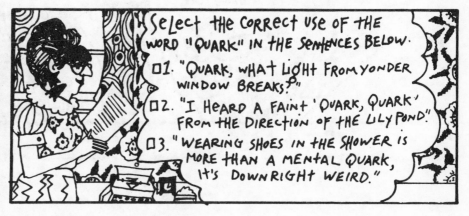

SELECT THE CORRECT USE OF THE WORD "QUARK" IN THE SENTENCES BELOW.

☐1. "QUARK, WHAT LIGHT FROM YONDER WINDOW BREAKS?"

☐2. "I HEARD A FAINT 'QUARK, QUARK' FROM THE DIRECTION OF THE LILY POND."

☐3. "WEARING SHOES IN THE SHOWER IS MORE THAN A MENTAL QUARK, IT'S DOWNRIGHT WEIRD."

The Sylvia School of Writing

ADVANCED BONUS WORD: "GAMS"

PICK the CORRECT DEFINITION of "GAMS" BELOW.

☐ 1. the PINK STUFF ABOVE the teeth.

☐ 2. A RELATIVE of the SWEET POTATO.

☐ 3. the GRANDMOTHER OF A YOUNG SHEEP.

TOMORROW: USING the WORD.

MOVE OR DIE

Alien Love

the STORY CONTINUES.

I HAVE A SEASONAL SUPRISE FOR YOU, MY SWEET.

"I KNOW YOU'RE HOMESICK FOR EARTH AND ESPECIALLY CHICAGO THIS TIME OF YEAR", HE MURMURED (PRONOUNCING IT "DRCHIVAGO" WITH THAT DELIGHTFUL LISP THAT THE MEN OF HIS PLANET HAVE). HE LED ME OUT TO THE PATIO AND FLICKED A SWITCH... SLOWLY AND BEAUTIFULLY IT BEGAN TO SNOW. "LATER SOME MEN WILL COME AND FIGHT OVER PARKING SPACES," HE SAID, KISSING MY EYELIDS.

THE SYLVIA SCHOOL OF WRITING

LESSON 46: ENDING THE STORY.

COMPLETE THIS STORY IN SPANISH AND ENGLISH.

I WAITED FOR HER IN THAT SAME CRUMMY BAR EVERY NIGHT BECAUSE I KNEW SHE'D SHOW ONE NIGHT AND I'D BE WAITING. AND ONE NIGHT SHE DID, COMING IN ON A WAVE OF GARDENIA SCENT, AND FLASHING "THAT" SMILE, AND SAYING: "HI JOE," AS IF SHE HADN'T LED ME INTO A MORASS OF BETRAYAL, CORRUPTION, MURDER AND WORSE, AND I _____

I LOOKED FOR DOROTHY BLAIR IN EVERY HACIENDA WITHIN A 3-MILE RADIUS OF THE HOTEL EQUADOR, BUT I NEVER FOUND HER — YEARS LATER I HEARD THAT SHE _____

I PUT MY FOOT DOWN SHARPLY ON THE BRAKE; NOTHING HAPPENED EXCEPT THAT I _____

INSTRUCTIONS: FINISH THIS STORY USING VISITORS FROM OUTER SPACE.

NEXT WEEK: WRITING THE MIDDLE PART.

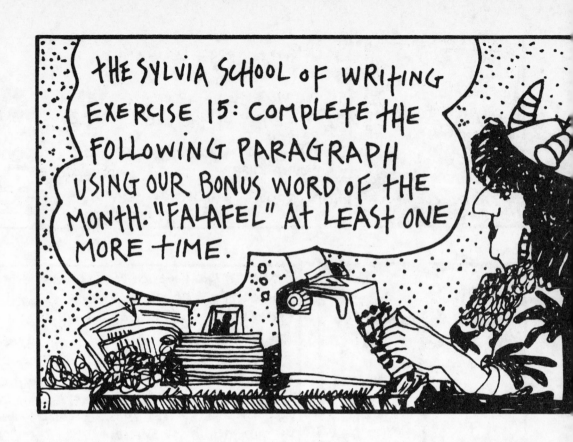

THE SYLVIA SCHOOL OF WRITING EXERCISE 15: COMPLETE THE FOLLOWING PARAGRAPH USING OUR BONUS WORD OF THE MONTH: "FALAFEL" AT LEAST ONE MORE TIME.

"THE PATH TO VIRTUE LIES AMONG THE BRAMBLES AND THE THICKETS." NO KIDDING.

BECAUSE I SAID SO! I DON'T KNOW WHY SOMEONE DOESN'T MAKE A FORTUNE COOKIE THAT TASTES GOOD. NOT EVERYONE FEELS OBLIGATED TO EAT THE COOKIE TO GET THEIR FORTUNE.

YOU KNOW WHAT WOULD MAKE A REALLY DYNAMITE FORTUNE COOKIE? AN OREO. YOU COULD PUT THE FORTUNE IN THE CENTER; EVERYONE TAKES THEM APART ANYWAY.

Alien Love CHAPTER 5: UNLOOKED FOR EVENTS

"COME HERE, I WANT TO SHOW YOU SOMETHING," HE MURMURED. HE OPENED THE DOOR TO A ROOM THAT WAS DECORATED IN PINK ORGANDY AND DOTTED SWISS. "THIS IS OUR BABY; I HAD IT YESTERDAY," HE SAID. "MY, I SAID HOARSELY, "YOU'RE FULL OF SURPRISES," AND FELL FORWARD INTO HIS ARMS, ARMS, ARMS.

I NEARLY FALAFEL MY CHAIR WHEN HE STOOD UP, AND I SAW THAT HE WAS NEARLY 7 Ft TALL. HE SPOKE, BUT I DIDN'T HEAR HIM, I WAS SO STUNNED BY HIS BEAUTY. LATER I FALAFEL ABOUT MY GAUCHERY AND I

THE MOTEL WAS A DIRTY PINK, CRAMPED AND FADED, LIKE A DWARF AMONG TALL TREES. I CLIMBED THE SCABROUS IRON STAIRCASE TO THE SECOND FLOOR. I WAS THERE TO MEET A CLIENT; I WAS LATE. I MOVED PAST DARK, DUSTY WINDOWS; WINDOWS LINED WITH FORGOTTEN FRUIT. FRUIT THAT ROTTED BEFORE IT RIPENED; VICTIM OF THE LACK OF LIGHT LIKE THE HUMAN ANTHROPOIDS THAT SHARED THEIR SPACE. *AND THEN I SAW HER. SHE STOOD IN THE SHADOWS, BUT EVEN IN THE SHADOWS SHE WAS SOMEHOW BOTH LIGHTER AND DARKER THAN HER SUR-ROUNDINGS.* THE NEON LIGHTS ON THE BOULEVARD BELOW FLICKERED AND DIED AS I REACHED OUT TO HER.

.......BEFORE YOU LEAP

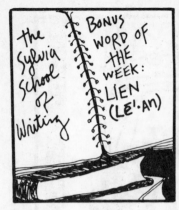

the Sylvia School of Writing

BONUS WORD OF THE WEEK: LIEN (LĒ'.AN)

SELECT THE CORRECT USE OF THE WORD: "LIEN"

☐ A. "DON'T YOU LIEN AGAINST ME, UNLESS YOU PLAN TO MARRY ME, SHE SAID TO THE MAN ON THE BUS." "O.K., I'LL MARRY YOU," HE SAID.

☐ B. "I'D LIKE A LIEN PIECE," SHE SAID TO THE CHEF. "AIN'T NO 'LIEN' ON A HOG" SNARLED THE CHEF.

NON!

THE SYLVIA NEWSLETTER OFFERS A CORRECTION AND AN APOLOGY FOR ITS PHOTO CAPTION WHICH ERRONEOUSLY IDENTIFIED MILES DONOVAN AS THE WINNER OF "THE SHORT STORY WRITER OF THE YEAR" AWARD. THAT AWARD ACTUALLY WENT TO SARAH LUCAS.

WE FURTHER APOLOGIZE THAT THE PHOTO USED WAS NEITHER MILES OR SARAH, BUT A PLATE OF RED BEANS AND GRAVY.

DO YOU KNOW YOUR NEWSPAPERS?

UFO LANDS ON DOG.

OH GO AHEAD!

WHAT NEWSPAPER IS THE PROBABLE SOURCE FOR THIS HEADLINE: "THE SOVIETS PLAN TO PUT A QUEEN ON THE THRONE."?
☐ THE NEW YORK TIMES
☐ GAY LIFE
☐ THE NATIONAL EXAMINER

Alien Love... CAN A WOMAN from a small TOWN IN THE MID-WEST FIND JOY ON ANOTHER PLANET?

LOVER.

ANGEL.

"COME SEE WHAT I GOT FOR YOU," HE CALLED FROM THE OTHER ROOM. "IT BETTER BE GOOD, I SAID, IT BETTER BE SOMETHING LIKE PLACIDO DOMINGO AND BARYSHNIKOV HERE TO DO A SONG AND DANCE."

IF FROGS HAVE TEETH, DO THEY GET CAVITIES?

"OH, YOU GUESSED," HE SIGHED.

She slapped him—he caught her arm and pressed her to him in a grip of steel; she felt his long arrogant taut thighs in his long taut jeans burning into her flesh. Her breath grew shallow; her nipples hardened, like two tiny pebbles, like sweet hard candy, like two finishing nails.

Oh how she hated him—Yet her body flamed with desire for him.

.... Wayward Nipples

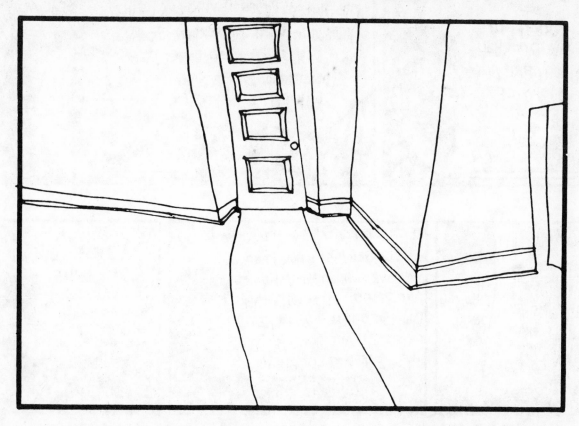

THAT ROOM WAS LOCKED...HAD BEEN FOR AS LONG AS SHE COULD REMEMBER. AT NIGHT WHEN THE HOUSE WAS STILL, SHE COULD HEAR SOMEONE MOVING AROUND IN THERE.

THUMP, THUMP.

THEY WARNED HER ABOUT WANDERING AROUND THE HOUSE AT NIGHT...

BUT AGAIN AND AGAIN SHE WAS DRAWN TO THAT DOOR.

NOW SHE TOUCHED IT AND IT SWUNG OPEN. A VOICE WHISPERED HER NAME... "FELICITY."

IT WAS WILLIAM POWELL, A SCOTCH ON THE ROCKS IN ONE HAND AND A PEACH SATIN PEIGNOIR, TRIMMED WITH MARABOU, IN THE OTHER...

OH YEAH.

TOUCH NOT THE DOORBELL. THE TERRIFYING STORY OF...

THE HOT-BLOODED DEVEREAUX FAMILY, THROBBING WITH PERVERSION, BRUTALITY AND DESIRE... PURSUED FOR THREE GENERATIONS BY A SAVAGE POST OFFICE EMPLOYEE.

THE SYLVIA SCHOOL OF WRITING EXERCISE 476 COMPLETE THE FOLLOWING PARAGRAPH:

"I COME IN PEACE", SHOUTED ARAKŌ TO THE CURSED METAPHOR PEOPLE WHO SURROUNDED HIM, WHINING AND PRODDING HIM WITH THEIR POINTED PITHOES. "WAIT," HE CRIED, "I HAVE BROUGHT BACK THE SACRED TALISMAN...."

AND SO SAYING, HE BROUGHT OUT A JADE BOX CONTAINING:
1. A BIC LIGHTER
2. A CONVENTIONAL NUCLEAR WEAPON.
3. OTHER.

SURVEY QUESTION ASKED OF 15 PEOPLE STARING INTO SPACE ON A BUS.

WHICH PIECE OF DIALOGUE BELOW HAVE YOU ALWAYS WANTED THE OPPORTUNITY TO SAY?
☐ 1. "BLINK YOUR EYES TWICE IF THE MURDERER IS IN THIS ROOM."
☐ 2. "THAT BLACK SEDAN HAS BEEN FOLLOWING US SINCE WE LEFT THE HOTEL, HANG ON TO YOUR HAT, I'M GOING TO LOSE HIM."

the SYLVIA SCHOOL of MYSTERY WRITING

COMPLETE THE FOLLOWING SENTENCE AND THEN WRITE 300 MORE PAGES.
"I RELIVE THAT EVENING AT FAIRHAVEN CASTLE EVERY NIGHT IN MY DREAMS, FOR IT WAS THERE THAT I LOST MY...
☐ INNOCENCE."
☐ CONTACT LENSES IN LORD MANDINGO'S CONSOMMÉ"
☐ POISE, AND, ALMOST, MY LIFE."

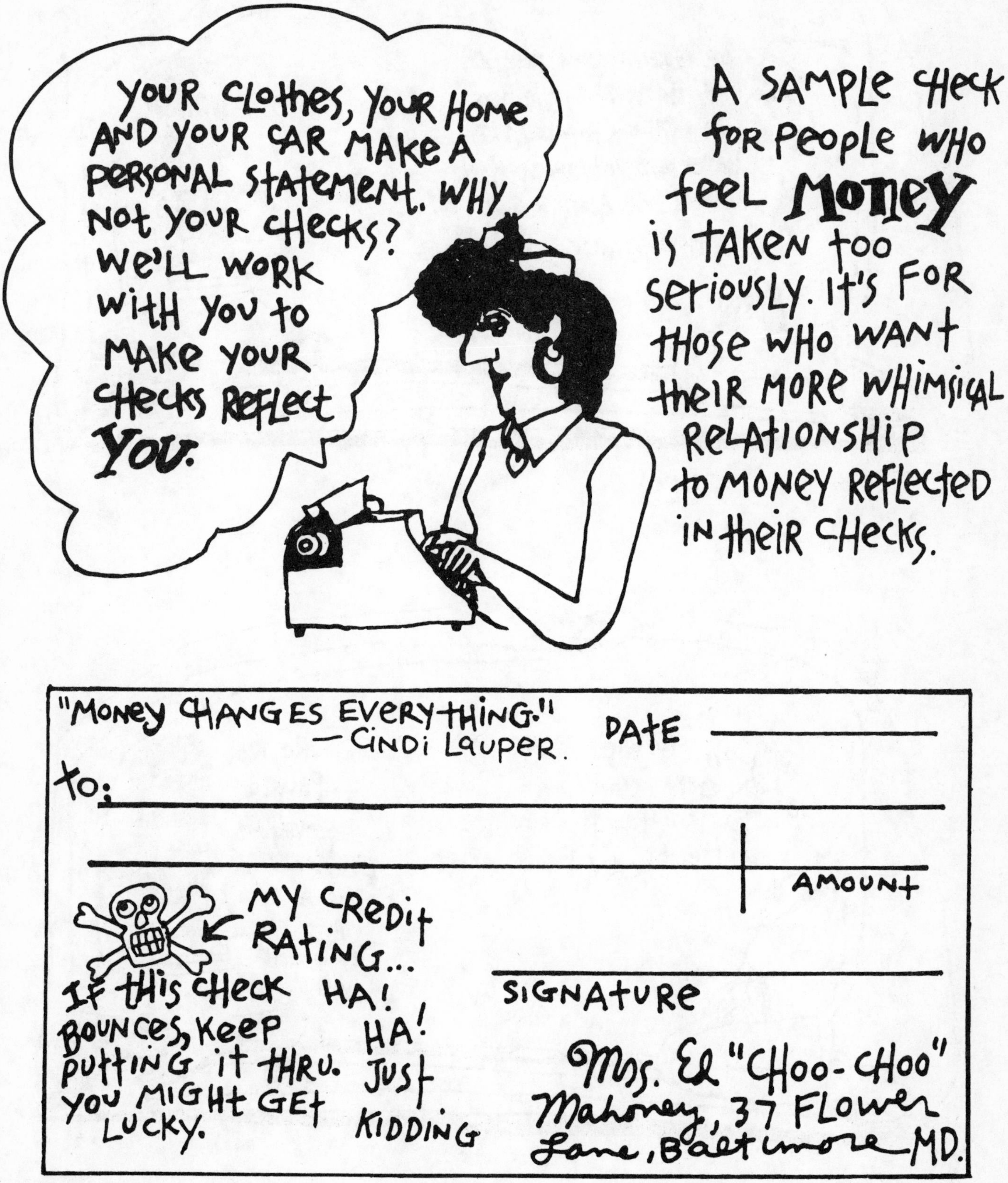

YOUR CLOTHES, YOUR HOME AND YOUR CAR MAKE A PERSONAL STATEMENT. WHY NOT YOUR CHECKS? WE'LL WORK WITH YOU TO MAKE YOUR CHECKS REFLECT YOU.
A SAMPLE CHECK FOR PEOPLE WHO FEEL MONEY IS TAKEN TOO SERIOUSLY. IT'S FOR THOSE WHO WANT THEIR MORE WHIMSICAL RELATIONSHIP TO MONEY REFLECTED IN THEIR CHECKS.
"MONEY CHANGES EVERYTHING." —CINDI LAUPER.
DATE
TO:
AMOUNT
MY CREDIT RATING...
IF THIS CHECK BOUNCES, KEEP PUTTING IT THRU. YOU MIGHT GET LUCKY.
HA! HA! JUST KIDDING
SIGNATURE
Mrs. Ed "CHOO-CHOO" Mahoney, 37 FLOWER Lane, Baltimore MD.

LITTLE KNOWN CONVERSATIONS BETWEEN HISTORICAL FIGURES

LIZZIE BORDEN AND HER MOM

IS SOMETHING BOTHERING YOU?

WHY DO YOU AXE?

OPEN LETTER TO MIKE WALLACE. RE: INTERVIEW WITH NANCY REAGAN ON "60 MINUTES" HEY! LAY OFF NANCY REAGAN! SO SHE'S SHALLOW, INSENSITIVE, SOMETHING OF A DIM BULB, AND RICH...

SINCE WHEN HAS THAT BEEN A CRIME IN THIS COUNTRY? SIGNED, A CONCERNED VIEWER

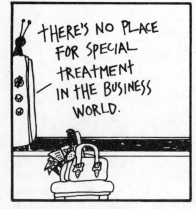

THERE'S NO PLACE FOR SPECIAL TREATMENT IN THE BUSINESS WORLD.

IF WOMEN WANT TIME OFF TO BEAR CHILDREN, THEY CAN'T EXPECT TO BE TREATED AS EQUALS.

OKAY, GIVE MEN TIME OFF TO BEAR CHILDREN.

TODAY JANET DUGAN OF N.O.W. IS WITH US IN OUR STUDIO TO ANSWER OUR AUDIENCE'S FAVORITE QUESTIONS ON E.R.A. LET'S HEAR FIRST FROM THE LADY IN BLUE. GO AHEAD MA'AM...

MY NAME IS ALMA PETERSEN, AND I JUST WANT TO SAY THAT IF THESE LIBBERS HAVE THEIR WAY, WOMEN WILL BE DRAFTED AND WHAT I WANT TO KNOW IS:

HOW'S A DECENT WOMAN GOING TO RELIEVE HERSELF ON THE BATTLEFIELD?

ALMA, WHY DON'T YOU TRY HOLDING IT UNTIL PEACE-TIME.

I'M SICK OF it! ANOTHER SEMINAR to teach BUSINESS WOMEN SPORTS AND WAR TERMS SO THEY CAN SOUND LIKE MEN... "ARMED to THE teeTH",

OPEN-toeD SHOES AND DANGLE EARRINGS

ARE NO NOS IN THE BUSINESS WORLD

"BLOODIED, BUT UNBOWED". FEH! WHEN ARE THEY GOING to teach MEN to SAY STUFF LIKE: "THIS DEAL'S AS WOBBLY AS A GIRAFFE IN FOUR INCH HEELS"?

BATTEN THE HATCHES GUYS, SHE'S ON THE WARPATH.

Ring! Ring!

Hi, THIS IS SYLVIA. ARE YOU AT WORK? DID YOU REMEMBER TO TURN THE IRON OFF BEFORE YOU LEFT FOR WORK? ARE YOU SURE? HAVE YOU SEEN YOUR CHECKBOOK RECENTLY? MAYBE YOU LEFT IT AT THE CLEANERS. MAYBE IT'S BEEN STOLEN. SEE, YOU REALLY DON'T FEEL MUCH LIKE CHATTING, AFTER ALL.

Commemorative Stamp
Ella Sue Whitney
First Woman to Smoke Dope on the Moon.

When asked if she felt the women's movement had anything to do with being honored with a commemorative stamp, Ms. Whitney replied: "Certainly not, I had the qualifications and I worked like hell for the distinction."

OKAY. I KNOW YOU'RE GOING TO FIND THIS HARD TO BELIEVE, BUT I'VE BEEN UP FOR HOURS. I WASHED THE FLOOR, I WROTE 2 CHAPTERS OF MY NOVEL...

WHAT'S GOOD?

PUPPIES, LITTLE CHILDREN LAUGHING, OLD MOVIES, WALKING IN THE RAIN...

I'M PROBABLY SAFE WITH THE GRILLED CHEESE.

CABBAGE A L'ORANGE TODAY.

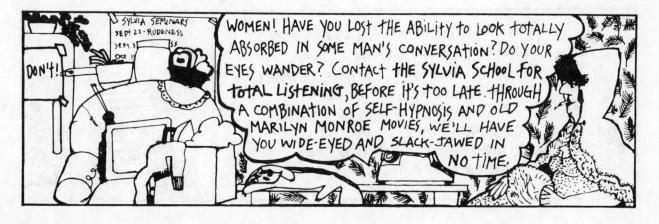

SYLVIA SEMINARS
SEPT 22 - RUDENESS

DON'T!

WOMEN! HAVE YOU LOST THE ABILITY TO LOOK TOTALLY ABSORBED IN SOME MAN'S CONVERSATION? DO YOUR EYES WANDER? CONTACT THE SYLVIA SCHOOL FOR TOTAL LISTENING, BEFORE IT'S TOO LATE. THROUGH A COMBINATION OF SELF-HYPNOSIS AND OLD MARILYN MONROE MOVIES, WE'LL HAVE YOU WIDE-EYED AND SLACK-JAWED IN NO TIME.

FANTASIES

WOMEN WILL SHAKE OFF THE INFLUENCE OF GODLESS COMMUNISM AND RETURN TO THEIR FIRST DUTY AS WIVES AND MOTHERS EARLY NEXT YEAR.

I'M 28 YEARS OLD... I'M PRETTY INDEPENDENT,

AND A LITTLE UNCONVENTIONAL IN MY DRESS.

I BET YOU CAN'T BELIEVE A WOMAN LIKE ME USES KOTEX.

I BET YOUR MOTHER CAN'T BELIEVE YOU DID THIS COMMERCIAL.

TODAY, THE PRESIDENT ANGRILY REJECTED STATISTICS SHOWING THAT IN 75% OF MIDDLE INCOME FAMILIES BOTH HUSBANDS AND WIVES WORK. HIS VOICE SHAKING WITH EMOTION, HE ASKED: "DOES NANCY WORK? DOES MISS ELLIE WORK? DID THE BEAVER'S MOTHER WORK?"

FIRST HE WANTS ME TO PUT ON BUNNY EARS AND PATENT LEATHER SHOES, THEN HE WANTS ME TO EAT A BACON, LETTUCE AND TOMATO SANDWICH.

UPPER WEST SIDE

I GO, "MISTER YOU ARE SO SICK. I DON'T DO NITRITES."

DAMN STRAIGHT

UPPER WEST SIDE

DEAR FRAZZLED,

ADVICE BY SYLVIA

NETWORKING AND DRESSING FOR SUCCESS ARE NOT ENDS IN THEMSELVES.

SOON YOU SHOULD START LOOKING FOR A JOB.

AN INVENTION WHOSE TIME HAS NOT YET COME.

"SCRATCH AND SNIFF" MONEY

thanks tom

WHEN YOU SCRATCH THEM, THE HUNDRED DOLLAR BILL SMELLS LIKE A DAY IN THE COUNTRY, AND THE DOLLAR BILL SMELLS LIKE A McDONALD'S HAMBURGER.

Mrs. ROSEMARY DAVIS with the CHECK DESIGNED FOR HER BY Sylvia.

I'M A VERY ROMANTIC WOMAN, AND I WANTED MY CHECKS to REFLECT THAT.

Mrs. Rosemary Davis
PERSONAL CREDO: "I Believe in Love"

DATE _____
PAY to A WONDERFUL PERSON/COMPANY:

the SUM OF: _____

_____

Signed _____
With Warm Personal Regards